Y0-CCS-964

Fiddlesticks and Freckles

*The Forest Frolics of
Two Funny Fawns*

by

SAM CAMPBELL

The Philosopher of the Forest

ILLUSTRATED BY HARRY H. LEES

PACIFIC PRESS PUBLISHING ASSOCIATION
Mountain View, California
Oshawa, Ontario

Copyright © 1955 by
The Bobbs-Merrill Company, Inc.
Printed in the United States of America
Library of Congress catalog card number: 55-10892

TO ROSEMARY

CONTENTS

CONTENTS—*continued*

FIDDLESTICKS AND FRECKLES

I

A-HUNTING WE WILL GO

"A-HUNTING we will go! A-hunting we will go ..." I sang the words in subdued tones as the bow of our canoe glided into the sands that outline the irregular north shore of our Wisconsin lake. The sun was just peering over the eastern horizon, heralding the coming of a lovely June day. Little beads of dew clung to the pine-needle tips, sparkling like diamonds in the growing light of dawn. The clean, cool, crisp forest air seemed charged with that feeling of vastness and antiquity so much a part of the charm and mystery of the north country. "Hi-ho the dario, A-hunting we will go," I sang on.

"Quiet, you warbling nimrod—or you'll come back with an empty game bag," Giny warned as she stepped out of the canoe. She steadied the light craft while I made my way ashore, my arms filled with heavy equipment. I silenced my singing, though the song kept on in my thoughts.

We pulled the canoe up on the beach and, carefully picking our way, moved cautiously beyond the shoreline trees into the large area we called the "Clearing." Here a crop of young balsam trees about a foot high covered the ground, growing lustily but too low to ham-

11

per vision. At the far side of the area ran a little-used, rutty forest road which had been cut through to aid in forest-fire control. This same road was the northern boundary of our game refuge. Beyond it legal hunting could be done at proper seasons; within it animals were protected at all times.

"Our happy hunting ground," Giny whispered. "Isn't it lovely with all the bright-green new growth on the balsam twigs? June in the forest! What a paradise it is!"

"Get the game bag open and ready," I interrupted, directing her attention to one side. "There is our first quarry."

At the edge of the Clearing near the base of a towering white pine appeared an unusually large doe, animated and beautiful. The full sunlight fell upon her bright red-brown coat, marking her prominently against the green forest background. Her manner was alert, her ears pitched forward, her white tail twitching nervously and her front feet occasionally pawing the ground.

"Steady there, my haughty lady," I said in a low voice as I made ready. "Look your best—you are about to be shot!"

"The shooting you do with that camera will never hurt anything." Giny laughed, then added quickly, "And your picture might just as well be of midnight in Mammoth Cave if you don't remember to take the lens cap off! Oh, Sam, will you never learn?" With a quick move she reached up to my movie camera which I was carefully focusing on the deer and snatched the protective rubber cap from my telephoto lens.

"It seems to me all this has happened before," I said sheepishly.

"Would you like me to tell you how many good pictures you have lost that way—the puma family at Grand Canyon, the moose in Canada, the bear in Alaska, the mountain sheep?"

"No, please!" I winced at the recollection. "Why dig up the past when the present is so promising? Let's forget all that." I pressed the exposure button on my movie camera and began recording the beautiful scene before us.

The action of the doe likely saved me from being chided more about my past photographic mistakes. The graceful creature was moving forward now, coming right our way. She stepped high like a trained horse at a horse show to walk over the balsam trees, and she nipped off some young leaves from a small pin cherry as she went along. Her ears were turning rapidly, seeking telltale sounds from the forest, and her eyes eagerly searched about the Clearing. There was a bit of anxiety in her manner. Then she discovered us. We were partly concealed by brush and by the fact that she was facing the rising sun.

"She sees us!" Giny whispered excitedly as the eyes of

the animal were directed our way, studying us intently.

"And still she comes on," I added, keeping the camera trained on her.

To our surprise she kept coming until half the distance which separated us had been covered. There she stopped and stood motionless as a statue while she continued to study us. The clicking of the camera, which must have been audible to her, did not frighten her in the least.

"Giny," I said, "do you realize who that animal is?"

"Bobette!" Giny exclaimed, catching the trend of my thinking. "Who else would act like that?"

We had raised Bobette as a fawn a few years previously. She was one of our most devoted pets and though she took to the wilds when she grew older, she continued to be friendly. We knew her by her behavior rather than any particular marking. She would permit us to come closer to her than would a strange deer though we could not get right up to her. With her it was thus far and no farther. When we passed the limit she had set, she would turn and walk away.

We tested the creature before us. Leaving our camera we advanced in her direction, talking in soft friendly tones. Much to our delight, she stood her ground. We continued to talk and walk. When we were fifty feet from her she showed a little nervousness. At forty feet she turned and moved away hesitantly. At thirty feet she walked a little faster but she did not run.

"Bless you, Bobette, it *is* you," said Giny. "And I

know what concerns you so much. Somewhere about here you have a baby, maybe two of them. You're looking for it or them, aren't you, pet? You're a good mother."

Bobette was a good mother. Each year we saw something of her family, sometimes just one wobbly-legged, speckled fawn, but usually two of them. Bobette brought them through and it wasn't easy. Back in this forest live coyotes, wolves and wildcats which pose a constant threat to helpless fawns. Bobette was wise in her guidance and courageous in her defense of her young.

The big doe paused and looked back. Now her attention was directed beyond us across the Clearing to the edge of the heavier timber.

"There are youngsters around somewhere," Giny insisted. "I just know it."

We began weaving our way through the little trees, going in the direction Bobette was looking.

"See, what did I tell you?" Giny laughed delightedly, pointing toward a clump of alder brush. There stood a very young fawn staring at us with big baby eyes that showed no fear whatever. The sunlight struck her fully and revealed an amazing array of spots on her reddish-brown coat.

"You little beauty!" Giny exclaimed. "Sam, look at that sweet innocent expression, those big eyes, that lovely face!"

"And it looks as if she'd been caught without an

umbrella when it was raining paint," I added. "Fawns are supposed to have speckles, but this one has more than her share. She's just one mass of spots from head to foot. Hi there, little Freckles—stick out your tongue, I'll bet you have some on that."

"Freckles—a good name for her!"

"O.K., Freckles it is," I agreed. "If this is Bobette's offspring, we may see her often and need a name."

"Look! Look! Look!" Giny cried, gripping my arm. "There's another one. What a funny walk!"

Out of the woods walked the sauciest-looking fawn I ever laid eyes on. His head was erect, his ears forward, and he bent his legs needlessly high as he strutted out into the open. He reminded me of a peacocklike drum major who, with pompous step and twirling baton, leads the parade. The snooty creature paid no attention to us whatever.

"Is that real?" Giny asked. "Do you see what I see?"

"I do," I said, squinting at the creature. "Of all the conceited things I ever looked on, he is the worst. What a waddle! What a strut! He reminds me of a boy I used to know in the city. He thought he was pretty smart too and used to walk like that."

"What was his name?"

"I don't remember, but whenever we saw him we would say: 'Aw, Fiddlesticks!' "

"Fiddlesticks! That's just what I wanted to say to him," said Giny, laughing and pointing to the creature.

"Fiddlesticks and Freckles. The names go well together. Look at Bobette. These are her youngsters all right. See how concerned she is?"

Bobette gave out that strange whistling snort that is the alarm note of the deer. She pawed the earth with her feet. Human friends are all right in certain circumstances, but she didn't want her offspring getting too close to them. Again and again she gave the warning snort. She trotted a few steps toward the woods and then came back again. She stamped her feet and bounced up and down.

Freckles was plainly affected by these maternal messages. In a series of well-timed moves she worked her way to a point from which she could circle us and reach her mother. Choosing a moment when our attention was directed elsewhere, she made a sprint across the Clearing, ending behind the anxious doe. Not so did Fiddlesticks. Such concern was beneath his dignity. While his poor mother almost snorted her nose off, he calmly and deliberately walked across the Clearing, passing within twenty feet of us. He wore a most smug and self-satisfied expression as he paraded before us, lifting his feet high with each step, and saying by his every action, "Step aside, you common things, and let someone important pass by." Bobette scolded and stamped but he took his own sweet time.

When her twins were safe beside her, Bobette released some pent-up emotions. She gave Fiddlesticks as neat a spanking as any child of the wilds ever received. With her front feet she struck him several blows that hurt his pride as well as parts of his anatomy. Then she gave Freckles a spanking just on general principles, and all three disappeared into the woods.

Laughing repeatedly at what we had seen, Giny and I walked slowly over to the roadway. In the soft sands were tracks made by both small and large deer feet, no doubt the record of Bobette and her twins. There were tracks made by a rabbit too.

Giny followed these for a few feet, and then suddenly called to me. "Sam, what kind of tracks are these? They're huge. Could it be a wolf?"

I came to her and looked on some very large prints pressed deeply into the sand. "Not a wolf," I commented, "nor a big dog. These tracks show no claws as would be the case if it were any doglike animal. It must be a soft-padded foot that made the track. There are four toes and the claws are retracted as only a cat can do."

"A cat?" asked Giny, excitedly. "Would a cat make a track that large?"

"Five inches across," I said, measuring the mark with a pocket tape. "More than twice the size of a wildcat track." I knelt beside the footprints and studied them carefully. "Giny," I said, looking up, "do you remember when and where we saw such tracks before?"

She pondered for a moment. "I seem to remember

something similar . . . in clay mud, a long time ago."
Then she added quickly, "The mountain lion, on the
north rim of Grand Canyon."

"Right!" I said. "I know of no other animal that
could make a print like that."

"But a mountain lion here? Isn't this out of his
range?"

"His original range covered this continent," I replied. "He has been seen as far south as Patagonia and
north into British Columbia. That's how he got so
many names: cougar, panther, painter, puma, cata-
mount, mountain lion. I believe the Wisconsin state
records show the last one killed here in 1888, though
there have been unverified reports of them occasionally
since that time."

We followed the intriguing trail down the road. The
great beast had crossed and recrossed the sands, apparently hunting.

"What would he catch?" asked Giny.

"Deer, rabbits, woodchucks, farm stock—in fact,
anything short of a timber wolf or a bear."

"And man?"

"No. Seldom if ever is he known to attack a human

being. The early pioneers gave him a bad reputation, probably because of his huge size and his terrifying cry. But he's a coward before men. Oh, oh—look at this."

There were some other large-sized tracks alongside those of the cat. In the moist sand of the road were perfect patterns of the feet of two animals.

"Now you can compare the wolf track with that of the cat, or whatever he is," I said. "This one belongs to a huge timber wolf. The two tracks are about the same in size, but the toenail is evident in the wolf print and not in the other."

"Do you suppose one was stalking the other?" asked Giny, and she stooped to look at the interesting record.

"No, the wolf passed by here earlier," I observed. "See, there are rain marks in his tracks, but none in the cat's. He was here before the rain—two days ago."

"And the cat?"

"Last night, I believe."

"You're convinced it's a panther, aren't you?"

I shook my head. "I just don't know what else it can be."

Back at our cabin we searched our textbooks for information about the panther. We refreshed our memories about his habits, how he is a wandering creature, hunting over great areas of country. Perhaps our mystery creature was a casual visitor, merely passing through our forest. Or maybe he had selected the forest-covered hills at the head of our lake as his home.

Someday we would know—perhaps. So far he was just an intriguing mystery.

When the purple shades of night closed over the north country we paddled along the lake shores in our canoe. The rich gloom was charged with quiet charm and peace. Yet that great realm of darkness looked different now. There was a potential there that stirred our imaginations and kept us speculating and supposing. Somewhere in the secret recesses of this ebony mansion there was a great cat, possibly some seven feet long, weighing nearly two hundred pounds. He could move about the forest halls as silently as the shadows themselves. Right now he might be looking out at us with those feline eyes that can pierce the night.

"Only one thing keeps me from thoroughly enjoying the thought of his being there," said Giny softly.

"What's that? You're not afraid, are you?"

"Not for myself. What about Bobette? What about Freckles and Fiddlesticks? They live in constant danger."

It was an unpleasantness which bothered me too. But perhaps Bobette already knew more about all this than we did.

II

ANYONE SEEN OUR CAT?

OUR FOREST cabin nestles in a heavy growth of mixed north-woods flora on a three-acre island. The lake in which the island rests is less than a half mile wide so we are fairly close to every shore. The island is our front yard, the mainland our back yard.

This year Giny had a flower garden in her front yard. She had always wanted one there, but the island wasn't a very good host to flowers. The soil was thin, the foliage heavy, keeping back the sunlight, and flowers would rather dwell elsewhere. This season we made heroic efforts to encourage a few blossoms. We carried soil in by hand, fertilized it, raked it, hoed it, petted it, and pleaded with it. As a result, the inventory showed that Giny had six trilliums, four wild lilies of the valley, three sprigs of phlox and two tulips, all in various stages of growth and development. All of them looked as if they didn't enjoy life on the island very much. But Giny loved them and that is probably why they held on.

We returned often to the Clearing as spring advanced. However, nature, who is a good storyteller, for some time gave us nothing new on our mystery animal. She let us ponder the few things she had revealed to us to deepen our interest and intensify our yearning for more. The strange tracks were slowly erased, the sands dried by the sun and drifted by the winds.

The only evidence of anything unusual in the Clearing was the behavior of Bobette. This might have been only our imagination.

"She seems so nervous," Giny observed as early one morning we stood watching our family of deer walking, feeding and playing among the young balsams. "See how she keeps looking all about the place, never feeding calmly? Could she be watching for that cat?"

"It seems to me too that she is more tolerant of our presence."

"Wants us closer, doesn't she?"

"Yes, as though she felt more secure near us."

We walked slowly toward the doe. She saw us coming, studied us intently for a moment, then with what might have been a sigh of relief, bent her head to the ground and began eating tender young shoots. Freckles and Fiddlesticks saw us too. Their play came to an abrupt stop. They glanced at their mother for some sort of signal. Receiving none, at least none that we could recognize, they focused their attention on us. They stood so close together they looked like one animal with four huge ears.

Suddenly Freckles became imbued with an uncontrollable spirit of play. Apparently she wanted Fiddlesticks to join her in a romp. She jumped right up in the air, and then bounded sideways a few steps, twisting and tossing her pretty head in a silly sort of way. Fiddiesticks never budged. Freckles trotted back and playfully poked him with her front feet. No response from his royal highness—he just stood there with his eyes fixed on us, his ears forward, and his tiny white tail wigwagging saucy messages.

Freckles tried a new maneuver. She ran circles around her smug little brother. He was unimpressed. Then along with running she began to do jumps and side steps that suggested the cavorting of the loon. Fiddlesticks wouldn't so much as glance her way. In desperation she began leaping high in the air, wiggling, twisting, and shaking from one end of her graceful little body to the other—a kind of north-woods hula dance. Fiddlesticks totally ignored her, and she sank to the ground frustrated and panting. He stood still as a statue.

"Maybe he's stuffed," I suggested.

"No, he can move," said Giny. "He's just being dignified."

"Yes, and smug and snooty," I added.

Fiddlesticks was moving now, slowly and reluctantly. In his finest dress-parade steps he began a strutty walk toward his mother. He held his head high and his front feet curled as he lifted them to step over grasses and small trees. Freckles watched him critically, and Bobette ceased her eating to glance his way with an expres-

sion that seemed to say, "Could that be a child of mine?"

Then the whole scene of pomp and display underwent a sudden change. Fiddlesticks brought one of his fancy steps down too close to a ruffed grouse that was hidden beneath some tangled grass. The bird took off with that flurry of wings that makes one of the most startling sounds of the forest. Fiddlesticks, forgetful of all his assumed pride and posture, jumped to one side and with a frightened baby bleat raced for his mother. His front feet got tangled in some brush and he fell flat on the ground. He wasn't hurt in the least, but it was a terrible jolt to his dignity. He struggled to his feet and raced for the woods. Freckles followed, but she couldn't catch Fiddlesticks. Bobette followed too, plainly concerned about her two offspring. Deadly danger might well lurk in that woods, where the possibility of an ambush was much greater than in the Clearing.

Giny and I had a wonderful time as the sole spectators of this show. Our laughter that followed the fawns into the forest was loud enough that it probably hurried their flight.

"Did you ever see an egotist taken from his high horse more quickly than that?" she asked, looking after them.

We saw no more of them that day.

We told only our closest friends about the huge tracks

we had seen on the roadway in the Clearing. I thought it likely there was still a heavy bounty offered by the state for the panther, and I did not want to bring an army of bounty seekers into the area.

However, we questioned others as to the possibility of panthers and came upon some strange stories. Officially the state denied that such creatures were still in the northern forests. Reports of people seeing them had been received, but when investigated these all proved to be false, the animal involved generally being the Canada lynx.

From a game warden I got a very different story. He eyed me peculiarly when I asked him if he had heard of any panthers being in the country. "I have never seen one here," he said firmly, "but I was well acquainted with the animal in the west. One month ago . . ." He paused and looked at me as though wondering if he should continue, then went on. "One month ago I was up in the Brule River country on a mission. I slept out in my sleeping bag for three nights. The first night I awakened several times with the feeling that something was near me. Once I sat up and flashed my light about. I didn't see a thing but I distinctly heard something moving about in the brush. The next morning I found tracks that big. . . ." He circled his fingers to indicate about a five-inch track. "They came within six feet of my bag. Two nights later the same thing happened. This time the tracks came within a foot of me."

"Not wolf tracks?" I questioned.

"Definitely not," he said emphatically. "They showed no claw marks. I have had cougars come close to me that way in the west. They don't mean to attack. Just curiosity, I guess. But it gives you a funny feeling."

"You think this was a cougar then?"

He shrugged his shoulders. "Didn't see it," he said, "but what else could it be?"

I asked my question of a forest ranger.

"Panther in this country? No!" he said, without hesitation. "Haven't been any since 1888," he quoted official statistics. He was thoughtful for a moment and then added, "Had a funny experience once. I was in the back-tracker country hunting a smoke that had been reported. Got caught by the dark and had to stay out overnight. Had about a half-moon that night, and it gave pretty good light. Sometime near morning I woke up, feeling that something was near me. My flashlight didn't work when I tried to turn it on, but by the moonlight I could see a good-sized animal running. It was about the size of a deer but it didn't run like a deer and I felt sure I saw a long tail on it." He laughed. "No doubt it was a deer and some shadow effect made it look like it had that tail. I can never forget it."

"Any tracks," I asked.

"No—ground was covered with duff and it wouldn't show tracks. Funny how things will look to a fellow at night. I can still see that animal, long, low, and that tail!" His manner convinced me that he was not certain his experience had been with a deer.

An old trapper listened to my question. He scratched his head, but likely this was for reasons other than thought. "Found a deer carcass last win'er, been treated like a cat does," he said. "Been dragged too, mebbe fifty feet. Somethin' mighty strong."

"Any tracks?"

"Nope. Done in snow an' all drifted over. I didn't look much—was after beaver."

"Well, how does the evidence add up?" asked Giny after my inquiry had been going on a few days. "Do we have a panther or don't we?"

"Nothing conclusive, one way or the other," I replied. "But my opinion is that we'd better guard Bobette and her twins as closely as we can."

III

HAWAII CALLS AND BIRDCALLS

NATURE strayed into a period of mild and lazy June loveliness. Clear, azure skies let the strong sunrays caress the countryside, and wild flowers sprang forth on the forest floor at their touch. A feeling of harmony and peace prevailed that made us partially forget our mystery animal, even as weathering had removed his tracks from the sand. Bobette and her twins seemed relieved too. We saw them often at the Clearing and met them on several hikes. They were becoming more accustomed to us and a bit more friendly.

One day we had an amusing adventure with Fiddlesticks. Giny carried a birdcall whistle, a device that gives out a series of squeaks with a certain birdlike quality. These squeaks have brought wild birds within a few feet of us and occasionally have attracted other small animals.

"Let's see what effect it will have on his royal highness," said Giny as we saw the haughty fawn out in the Clearing a few yards from us.

She gave the device a few turns and at the shrill sounds Fiddlesticks' head went up. Other heads came up too. Both Bobette and Freckles were lying out of sight among the balsam trees. They stretched their

necks high to see what was producing this strange new
sound. Seeing us—a very ordinary and unexciting
sight—they reclined again to bask undisturbed in the
June sun.

Not so with Fiddlesticks. The squeaks fascinated
him. Ears pitched forward, he started one of his fancy
walks right toward us. Giny ground out calls that ran
all over the scale like the rambling song of the purple
finch. Fiddlesticks was so intrigued he forgot his surroundings. Stepping high, wide and handsome, he
came on as if drawn by an irresistible attraction. The
artificial birdcalls affected him as the siren songs of
mythology affected Ulysses. He had no wax to put in
his ears like the hero of old. His whole attention was
directed to the sounds, though likely curiosity rather
than musical appreciation governed him.

"Oh, Fiddlesticks, your eyes are as big as saucers!"
Giny laughed as she gave the birdcall some violent
twists that produced something like the voice of a rusty
gate.

Fiddlesticks seemed not to see us at all. That mysterious whistle was his whole world for the moment. He
came so close we could almost touch him. In fact, I
did! My hand advanced very slowly until a finger came
in contact with his little nose. The effect was electric.
Suddenly the charmed fawn was jerked out of his
dream. Whatever pictures his imagination had compounded under the spell of the birdcalls were dissolved,

and he found himself in a position he was never supposed to be in. Three feet from him were human beings—friendly ones, to be sure—but Mother had told him in her own way to be careful of such creatures. Some of them were all right, some of them were not, and it is good deer philosophy to keep all of them at a respectful distance.

Fiddlesticks was utterly flabbergasted. His mouth dropped open in surprise. He couldn't believe his eyes, so he tried his nose. Yes, there was the scent of human beings. Those laughing figures before him must be real. He tried to run, but at first his legs wouldn't move. He wiggled his tail furiously and managed to get out a little snort. And then—horror of horrors!—here came that hand reaching for him again, the very one that had touched his nose! This thawed out his legs and he whirled about so violently he nearly upset himself. Away he raced, bound for somewhere else, he didn't care where. After him came the squealing birdcall, but it had lost its spell over him. He ran right past his astonished mother and whizzed by his sun-bathing sister. They, not knowing whether he had stirred up a panther or a dinosaur, joined in the exodus. It was one wild flight that ended in the edge of the far timber. There we saw Bobette deal out a spanking. She knew Fiddlesticks needed it, even if she didn't know why. And our laughter mingled with squeaks made by Giny's playful twists of the birdcall.

"Let's read this one first," said Giny later, choosing a letter from the stack that arrived one morning.

"And why that one?" I asked.

"It's postmarked 'Hawaii.'"

Yes, that fact gave the letter priority. Hawaii had laid hold on our hearts ever since our first visit to that beautiful and friendly cluster of islands.

"Lahaina, Maui," Giny read the postmark. "Remember it?"

"Who could ever forget such a place?" I replied with an exaggerated sigh. "The flowers, the blue ocean, the palm trees and those wonderful friendly people."

"And do you remember little Moke?"

"Yes—Moke. Bless his heart!"

"Well," said Giny, unfolding a sheet taken from the envelope, "this letter is from Moke."

"No! Why, he is only five years old."

"Yes, just five and his letter looks like it." Giny wore a broad smile as she held out a sheet covered with pencil marks that looked like the trail of an earthworm. Likely the pencil had been held dagger-fashion by a childish hand and scrubbed back and forth until the paper was covered with a script that only the writer could read.

"Do you remember how he did his little version of the hula dance?" Giny laughed.

"Yes I do and also the way he called 'Aloha' so loudly and plainly," I replied, "and he always put a little extra emphasis on the 'ha.'"

"Look," Giny observed, "he has printed A L O H A on the other side. Or I guess that is what it is. Probably the only word he can write."

In red pencil and huge outlines were some drawings that could pass for the letters of Aloha, provided the reader was acquainted with that much-used Hawaiian word of greeting and knew that it was likely to be in every letter and conversation. There was a badly crippled "A," and an "L" that didn't know which way to go, an "O" that looked as if the pencil had got lost on its way around, an "H" that resembled a bird track, and another "A" that we had to take for granted.

"Aloha, Moke," Giny said aloud as if thinking her voice could carry over the more than four thousand miles that lay between us and the islands. "Aloha to your sweet little Hawaiian heart."

"Aloha, Moke," I echoed. "Please stay a child until we can get back and have one more look at you."

My thought pictured the happy, dark-skinned youngster as we had seen him at a social gathering on the island of Maui. He came with his attractive and talented mother Liliana. She sang for us at the request of our hostess. So did Moke. In fact, no one could make him stop! He broke into song every few minutes and as he sang he danced. His baby hands had the grace of native dancers, a quality that must be inherited rather than learned.

Liliana and Moke were full-blooded Hawaiians.

Their joyousness was contagious. Yet, there was tragedy in the family background, of which we learned. The husband and father had gone to serve his country in Korea. Later came the sad news that he would never return. Liliana, with the courage of her kind, faced the circumstance without ever losing her beautiful smile. Devotion to Moke became her whole life. A small home was left her, one built by her husband's own hands. There was a modest income from his insurance. She planned to be with Moke constantly until he reached school age, then there would be some time free in which she could increase their income. She could teach school, and she could sing.

I never saw a youngster radiate more love than Moke. His dark eyes danced with enthusiasm whenever anyone looked at him and he broke into a smile that hollowed out a dimple in each cheek. He loved everyone and he had perfect confidence that everyone loved him. Of course, everyone did.

Moke is the nearest the Hawaiian language can come to producing the name *Moses,* and *Liliana* is what it does to *Lillian.* The Hawaiian language has only twelve letters to work with: five vowels, *a, e, i, o, u,* and seven consonants: *h, k, l, m, n, p,* and *w.* So it has to reshape English words a bit.

We met Moke and his mother on several occasions and felt ourselves drawn closer and closer to them. On our return to the mainland, I sent Moke a set of my ani-

mal storybooks, and these seemed to open up an entirely
new world for him.

In the envelope received that morning was also a letter from Liliana. Giny read it aloud: "Moke's scribbling will need translation," the letter ran. "You may
not believe it, but every scratch means something. He
worked so hard to get this written. He is telling you
that we have read your book *Loony Coon* aloud and it is
maikai nui nui (very good). He wants to know what a
raccoon is—since we do not have them here. He wants
you to bring him one. He is so fond of animals. He says
to ask you to bring him also a porcupine, a skunk, a fox,
a bear, a snake, a woodchuck, a beaver, an otter and all
the other kinds you mention in your books. So you see
you will have to build a sort of Noah's Ark, fill it up
and sail over! Most of all he wants you to come and see
his pet chicken Ewa and mongoose Kimo. They grew
up together and are good friends—which is quite remarkable when you realize that mongoose like to feed
on chickens. Ewa means Eva, and Kimo means Jim. I
wish you could come and see them, though I suspect it
should be rather soon, for I don't like the way Kimo
looks at Ewa once in a while.

"Seriously, couldn't you come? Moke talks about
you constantly and we all feel as if you, or parts of you
at least, belong to Hawaii. Sincerely, Liliana."

"A pet mongoose . . . friendly with a pet chicken," I
mused.

"The mongoose comes from India, doesn't it?" asked Giny.

"Yes. It was introduced into Hawaii to control rats, which had come aboard ships. The rats are constantly a threat to Hawaiian chickens. In his home country the mongoose is pretty rough on rats, but in Hawaii it was easier to hunt chickens, so he lets the rats alone and just doubles the problem of the chicken raiser."

This was rather idle chatter. Neither Giny nor I was thinking much about what we were saying. Our thoughts played about the rocky shores of those distant islands, looked upon their fields of pineapple and sugar cane, watched the Hawaiian swimmers with their surfboards and outriggers, listened to the voice of the dove, the myna bird and the thin call of the diminutive iiwi.

"It would be wonderful to see the islands again," Giny broke the silence.

"And I *do* need more pictures for my Hawaii lecture," I added.

"And we *do* have some open time during the winter." Giny straightened up and looked at me hopefully.

The realization crept over us that this was a possible and practical thing to do. "Aloha!" I cried, rising to my feet and giving a very poor imitation of a hula dance. "Aloha! We are going to Hawaii! Let's get packed. . . ."

"Down, Fido, down." Giny laughed. "It is next winter we are going, not now."

"Oh-h-h-h-h," I said, sobering slightly. "But the main thing is, we are going."

"Yes, but we have responsibilities here. Freckles and Fiddlesticks need us, you know. There may still be a panther out in the woods." Giny has a wonderful way of bringing me back to earth.

"All right," I agreed, "I'll take it easy, but we can have the pleasure of writing Liliana and Moke we are coming, can't we?"

We did write our Hawaiian friends, saying we would be there "when snow has come to stay in our Wisconsin woods." We learned later that when this was read to Moke, he asked his mother what snow is. To appreciate her problem at that moment, she suggested that some-time we try to describe snow to someone who has never seen any.

Moke couldn't get the idea of rain coming down in any other form than that which fell on his island of Maui, and he finally suggested that we bring a package of snow when we came.

IV

OF COONS, CANS, TURTLES AND TRUCKS

I<small>F</small> G<small>INY</small> and I had known what that day had in store for us, likely we would have stayed in our beds. An energetic and enthusiastic redheaded woodpecker gave us little choice in that, however. At exactly 4:30 in the morning he came winging up to our downspout, and, regardless of the fact that it was made of unyielding metal that bore no resemblance to the bark of a tree, he gave it a pecking that sounded like a machine gun. It wasn't the first time this feathered alarm clock had beat his *rat-ta-tat-tat* on this spout. Every morning, except when it rained, he was there, and how his head and beak stood that beating we couldn't imagine. Apparently he liked it, though, and as if to make sure that the whole forest world was properly disturbed he would return two or three times to drum out his message.

"Couldn't the redheaded nuisance skip this one morning?" I grumbled sleepily. "We didn't get back from our canoe trip until three this morning. I barely got to sleep when old hardhead started his rumpus."

Rat-ta-tat-tat, rat-ta-tat-tat went the woodpecker on his second visit to the downspout.

Then suddenly there was a terrific crash, drowning

out the relatively mild efforts of the bird. Giny and I sat up in bed.

"What in the world was that?" she asked, rubbing her eyes.

"I think I know—only too well," I said resignedly.

"Well, what?"

"Oh, last night I thought I would put the garbage can where the raccoons wouldn't tip it over," I said. "It was full of tin cans and broken glass."

"Where did you put it?"

"On the roof of the little shed. I thought they wouldn't find it there."

We dressed and went out of our cabin to look on an

awful mess. The garbage can had been tipped over all right, and the ground was strewn with cans, glass and the miscellany that such refuse cans receive.

"A half day's work." I groaned as I looked on the widely strewn debris.

"There's the one who did it." Giny pointed to the edge of a balsam thicket. "Mr. Innocence himself. No doubt he will help you clean it up."

There sat a large-sized raccoon looking at me unafraid, as if asking what all the excitement was about.

"Yes, you, Loony Coon," I grumbled. "I suppose you just heard the noise and came over to see what happened. It couldn't be that you had anything to do with it. You weren't on top of that roof, were you, and you didn't pull on that garbage can until it rolled off and made a junk heap out of our yard? Not you—you never do such things! Come over here while I skin you alive."

Loony Coon came, the very picture of self-confidence. His left ear drooped, a distinguishing mark by which we identified him during the years he was our pet. He stopped once to yawn, wash his paws, and scratch back of an ear—just to show me that my mood didn't alarm him. Then he walked up to me to receive the petting and nibbles of peanuts he knew would be there. This ceremony completed, he curled up comfortably in the sun to watch me while I gathered up the rubbish he had spilled and consigned it once more to the large can.

"I hope your fur coat gets moths in it!" I flung at

him, as I finished the clean-up job and went in to my breakfast.

A part of this day had been budgeted to the painting of a rowboat. Everything was in readiness and the time was ripe. The boat had been placed on two wooden horses, and was properly dried for the occasion. I brought the brushes and the gallon pail of paint down to the scene of action, and also my tool box so that I could remove the seats and braces. Loony Coon watched these preparations for a few minutes, then, deciding it was all very boring, he crawled under the shed to sleep the day away, as a raccoon should.

"Have some nice nightmares about tipped-over garbage pails and such things," I taunted him as he disappeared. "If you forget and sleep an extra two or three days, it'll be all right with me."

New paint brightens up the world so wonderfully, I wonder why we don't use more of it. With the first few strokes of the brush I could see what a change was coming about in our old rowboat. I planned to make the boat green, with the exception of the seats, which would be finished with clear varnish. I placed the seats to one side out of the way, while in an inexpert way I began applying the green paint. Every brush load had its improving effect and it was easy to work up enthusiasm in what I was doing.

Giny called me to hang out our camp blankets for an

airing. I stretched a clothesline between two trees and thereon placed the red wool covers that had been a part of so many journeys back into the north country. As I went back to my painting job, I passed Loony Coon. "Thought you were asleep, young fellow," I commented. He paid no attention to me, but continued in the direction from which I had come. I thought there was something a bit unusual about his appearance, but I did not look closely.

Things down at the boat looked strange too. I couldn't find the can of paint at first. I had left it on a box, right beside my tool kit. When I discovered it, an unrestrained groan escaped me. The whole gallon of paint, minus the few brushfuls I had used, had been tipped over and was liberated to flow freely where it would. There were a couple of inches of it in my tool kit. Wrenches, hammer, drill, saw, pliers, screw drivers, nails, screws, sandpaper, steel wool—all rested in the luxury of a bath of soft, green paint. The ground had its share too, and right in the middle of this unnaturally colored sand, grit and goo was my paintbrush. Suffering from shock and helplessness, I picked up the brush and inanely watched it while it dripped green spots on my trousers.

"Pretty, isn't it?" said a voice behind me.

I looked about to see Giny watching me, her poorly suppressed amusement bursting through her lips and her eyes.

"Who did this?" I asked furiously. "If I find out, I'll——"

"Look at those tracks on the boat seats, and you will know," she said aggravatingly.

There was no denying the evidence. In clear-cut outline were the tracks of Loony Coon, done in rich green paint. From here he had gone over to the boathouse and left his autograph all over the floor. Apparently he had waded in the paint after tipping the bucket over, and he had dragged his tail through too—for there were long streaks of green in among the footprints.

"And when you get through looking at all this," Giny was saying, "come see the blankets you hung out. He wiped his feet on them and left a most unusual pattern."

I put my head back and gave a howl that was supposed to sound like something or other in deep distress.

Rat-ta-tat-tat, rat-ta-tat-tat went the woodpecker on the old downspout.

Early evening found us at the Clearing. Bobette, Fiddlesticks and Freckles were all there. We watched them from behind the borderline brush, gaining more intimate views of their antics through our binoculars. They were especially carefree. Bobette browsed on tender leaves of young aspens and maples, paying little attention to her twins. Apparently the breeze bore them no tidings of danger close at hand.

Fiddlesticks and Freckles indulged in a game of tag.

They raced about the area in their nimble way, taking turns chasing each other. Fiddlesticks had his temperamental fits, however. Right in the midst of a romp he would come to a stop.

"Just look at that snooty little scamp," I said. "He even struts when he stands still."

"Holds his head up like a social snob," added Giny, looking at the creature through the glasses. "I swear that his eyebrows are raised. If I were Freckles, I would pull his nose."

Freckles did about everything short of that to coax her twin brother to romp again. She pounced at him like a puppy, then ran circles around him. He didn't move.

"The old stuffed shirt!" Giny laughed. "Whoops, there he goes. What struck him?"

Fiddlesticks and Freckles suddenly started a race toward Bobette. She glanced at them, and then went on with her eating, obviously not the least concerned. The fawns raced to her very flank, and then both started nursing on her with such violence that they nearly pushed her over.

"No reprimand from Mother," Giny observed. "Apparently those are good manners in their circle."

"Just a nice little dinner party," I added. "She feeds while they feed, and a good time is had by all."

While the feeding was going on, we moved quietly to the side of a hill from which we could watch the Clearing and at the same time get a good view of a lovely sunset in the making. Long red streaks like searchlights reached up from the western horizon, and little islands of clouds above us blushed a salmon pink. From here also we could see the roadway at the back of the Clearing. Presently Fiddlesticks and Freckles worked their way over there. Once on the road, Fiddlesticks began some odd maneuvers. He danced about, racing away from a certain spot and then running back to it. He was giving much attention to something on the ground.

"It's a turtle," I said, looking through the glasses. "Right at his feet."

"So it is," Giny agreed, studying the object through her binoculars. "Look out, little idiot, that thing will bite."

Fiddlesticks didn't hear her, of course, and if he had he wouldn't have paid any attention. He had to learn the hard way. His inquisitive nose went closer and closer to the turtle. Suddenly the turtle's head shot out and Fiddlesticks received a sharp bite on his royal nose. He jumped right up in the air, then turned and raced down the road, his dignity greatly offended. Fortunately the turtle did not hang on as a snapper sometimes does. In his unhurried way he went crawling off the road, contented at having taught his tormentor a lesson.

Fiddlesticks came to an abrupt stop and assumed one of his lordly poses. He looked back at the creeping turtle, apparently fascinated by it and wondering just what he should do to anything that treated him that way.

"I hear a car coming," said Giny.

"I hear it too," I agreed. "Apparently it is on this fire lane. Probably the warden."

"It's coming fast and sounds like a truck," Giny noted.

We had not long to wait. Presently a pickup truck came down the winding road at a pace too fast for such a backwoods highway. We both gasped as the car rounded a curve and came suddenly upon Fiddlesticks.

"Fiddlesticks, run!" Giny screamed.

"Jump!" I shouted.

Fiddlesticks did neither. He was in one of his spells. His eyes were focused on the vanishing turtle, and there he stood. In the twilight he was not easy to see. The driver of the truck noticed him when it was too late to stop. He hit the horn button and his brakes at the same time, but neither the honk nor the screech meant a thing to Fiddlesticks. He didn't move a muscle. In desperation the driver cramped his steering wheel far to the right. Missing the entranced fawn by a matter of inches, he endeavored to keep his car out of the drainage ditch at the side of the road, but the right wheels were already over the bank in soft sand. For a hundred feet he battled to keep upright, but lost the fight. His truck tipped over on its side before coming to a stop. Fiddlesticks still stood motionless.

"Did you ever see such an aggravating creature as that fawn?" Giny exclaimed, as she got her breath. "Come, that man may be hurt."

We hurried toward the car. The man wasn't hurt— that is, physically. He climbed out of the car and looked back at Fiddlesticks. "You long-eared idiot!" he shouted. "I'd like to pick your spots off one at a time.

You ought to be stuffed and in a museum. Look what you've done to my car—and I'm in a hurry to get home too!"

From the distance there came a warning snort. Bob-

ette was trying to get through to Fiddlesticks. Suddenly the situation dawned on the youngster. He heard us cracking brush as we walked toward the scene. He saw the man and the car. Away he went as fast as he could go for about fifty yards. Then he stopped and snorted out as neat a scolding as a man ever received.

It took us until almost midnight to get the truck straightened up. The car wasn't hurt, aside from a dented fender, and it ran under its own power. After his first exasperation, the driver wasn't greatly disturbed. His parting words were, "Well, he was a cute little rascal—glad I didn't hit him."

Giny and I were so exhausted we could hardly get ready for bed. "Do you suppose there is any place in the world where there are absolutely no animals?" I asked.

"Perhaps—but why do you ask?"

"If there is, I want to go there and live!" I declared.

Giny had strength enough for one last laugh. It was nearly 2:00 A.M. when we got to bed, and we slept until all of four-thirty when from the downspout we heard *Rat-ta-tat-tat, rat-ta-tat-tat.*

V

OF BIRDS, BEES AND ——?

WE WROTE to Moke giving him the story up to date of Fiddlesticks and Freckles, and enclosing snapshots of the animals. Deer would be new creatures to Moke.

The speed of the air mail between our north-woods Sanctuary and his island some 2,300 miles out in the Pacific was amazing. Three days after we had dropped our letter in the boxlike post office of our town, he held the letter in his dark little hands and looked with delight on the fawn pictures. Three more days and his reply was back to us, bearing pictures he had drawn of Ewa the chicken and Kimo the mongoose. At least, we guessed that was what the odd figures were on his scribbled-up paper. An accompanying letter from his mother verified our conjecture.

Kimo, as pictured by Moke, resembled a mongrel peanut more than a mongoose. He was oblong in shape, with two straight-line legs on top and two on the bottom. His head looked like a bubble that had somehow got attached, and his eyes were two dots on the paper totally separated from the main body. The tail resembled a long trail of smoke. At that, Kimo had fared better in Moke's portrait than Ewa the chicken. Apparently our budding artist had become quite discouraged at producing the peculiar contour of the fowl. We could see a sort of circle representing Ewa's body and two straight lines for legs at the bottom. But the making of the head was baffling, so Moke just scratched over it and said that that was Ewa behind a chicken coop.

Within the envelope was a folded piece of paper containing some white petals of a flower. "These are from the shower tree," said the letter of explanation from Liliana. "One day to help Moke picture snow I took a handful of these and let them drift to the ground while he watched them. Now every day he must have his snowstorm. I must climb on a chair so the 'snow' gets a greater fall. Usually this happens in the house, necessitating a removal operation afterwards. He insisted on my sending this 'snow' to you. He thinks if it is just snow you want, maybe now you can come right away."

Moke was sure we would bring Fiddlesticks, Freckles and Loony Coon, Liliana's letter went on to tell us. He was all prepared for them. The two fawns would live with Ewa, and Kimo would take Loony Coon to his home out somewhere among the banana trees.

Fiddlesticks, Freckles and Bobette looked very contented with their portion of the world when we saw them the next morning at dawn. They were in their beloved Clearing, making the most of every moment. Even Bobette was in playful mood, and danced about in the cute and cunning fashion usually limited to her fawns. The youngsters staged several races about the grounds and all went well—until Fiddlesticks ran afoul of a bumblebee. He was putting on one of his struts bringing him within a few yards of where we stood.

"Fiddlesticks, I do believe you have more spots than you had last time I saw you," said Giny, examining him through her binoculars. "And if possible you're snootier than ever before. You act as if no spot on earth is quite good enough for you to step on. Oh, oh—now what ails you?"

The spotted creature began prancing about in a strange manner, tossing and shaking his head.

"It's a bee," I said, watching through my glasses. "A huge northern bumblebee. Fiddlesticks must have stirred him up from the blueberry blossoms. Look out, Fiddlesticks, or you'll wring your own neck."

The bee was circling the head of the fawn, probably buzzing like a miniature airplane, and Fiddlesticks did his best to follow the insect with his eyes. Round and round went the bee, and round and round Fiddlesticks twisted his head. The fawn ran a few steps but the bee kept up with him. He rared up on his hind legs and struck at the aggravating thing, but he might as well have directed his blow at the wind. Now a bumblebee is not an aggressive creature, and usually his buzzing around is for his own amusement. If let alone, he will circle about for a time and then go his way.

"Be careful, Fiddlesticks," I called as both Giny and

I watched. "That fellow is dynamite. No—don't do that!"

Fiddlesticks was striking out again. His patience was exhausted, and he dealt one blow after another at the insect. Then the bee came to rest right on the fawn's nose. Fiddlestick's eyes widened like saucers. Giny was sure he looked cross-eyed. With a desperate move he wiped the bee off by brushing his head against a small balsam tree. Until that moment the bee had been having fun, but suddenly things were serious. He made a dive-bombing run at one of Fiddlestick's white spots near his tail and hit the target perfectly. No doubt the fawn's hair blunted the thrust of the stinger, but some of it reached the skin and Fiddlesticks received an urge to run as he had never traveled before. With a beautiful bound he cleared the balsam trees near him, and then he broke all existing records for the hundred-yard dash, ending in the woods. He reappeared almost immediately and crossed the Clearing again, breaking his own newly made record. Probably he had the feeling that the bee was still at that white spot, doing whatever a bee does to make a fellow miserable. But the old bee had forgotten all about it and was back gathering nectar among the blueberry blossoms.

"What a world you have to live in, Fiddlesticks," said Giny. "With turtles that bite your nose and bees that sting your spots, it must be hard to hold your kingly dignity."

Presently Fiddlesticks emerged again into the Clearing. He looked and listened all around to see if that jet-propelled insect was present. Then he staged a strut to his mother where he and Freckles helped themselves to dinner.

These were busy days in our forest Sanctuary. Patty Sausage, our old woodchuck pet who had undermined our front steps with her underground home, appeared with three fat, chubby, stupid youngsters. They played about the yard, climbed low balsam trees, scuffled with one another and ate amazing quantities of the cabbage and carrots Giny put out for them. They never strayed far from the entrance to their cave, however, and when anything frightened them they went down that hole so quickly it seemed they had just dissolved.

There was a new development in Giny's flower garden: a dandelion suddenly burst into bloom. Giny made it very welcome. "Just make yourself at home, little fellow," she said. "Folks don't like you in their lawns, but I like you and I think you're beautiful." The other flowers were making progress in a halfhearted sort of way.

Near the lake shore, fifty yards from our cabin, we found the nest of song sparrows. When we first saw it, there were two greenish, spotted eggs in it. The male bird sang loud and long, striving to draw our attention to him, while the female fluttered from tree to tree in a mood of mixed courage and caution. We were thrilled to have these wonderful little birds so close to us.

"Not a cent of rent do we charge them for the property," Giny insisted. "They'll pay their way with song."

Two days later she slipped up to have a peek into the nest. What she saw caused her to call me. "Sam!" she cried. "We have more tenants than we thought. Look in this nest."

I went to her and discovered that the large, brown-blotched egg of a cowbird had been deposited along with those of the song sparrow. The cowbird is a notable parasite in the raising of its young. Apparently these dusky birds believe in parental freedom and appoint their feathered neighbors as unwitting nursemaids. They place their eggs in nests of other birds, thus saving themselves the bother of building nests and hatching and feeding their offspring. This leaves the parent cowbirds much more time for social affairs, flying about in carefree manner and indulging in avian bridge, bugs, and entertainment. It is an imposition on the birds who raise their young for them, however, and frequently the baby cowbirds are so huge they force the legitimate heirs out of the nest.

"Are we going to permit this?" asked Giny, looking at the large egg. "Why, that little song-sparrow mother will have to work her feathers to frazzles to feed this imposter!"

I studied the situation for a moment. It was a great

temptation to take that cowbird egg out of the nest and halt this subtle villainy. Then I thought better of the idea.

"Perhaps this is an opportunity to learn something," I suggested. "This is going on all the time in the world of nature, and for us to interfere here wouldn't correct the general situation. This is where we can watch it. Do you mind if we just let things take their course?"

Giny consented, but she wasn't happy about the circumstances.

The air was filled with song-sparrow melody, and the mother bird came to the nest the moment we left. She settled down on the eggs, probably wondering what that unusual bump was beneath her.

So many things were happening we had nearly forgotten the huge tracks once found in the sands at the Clearing and our hypothetical panther. Once a story came to us that stirred renewed speculation. A young man of our town had been driving on a backwoods road a few miles beyond our Sanctuary. Coming to a little opening in the forest, he stopped his car and played his spotlight about the area, in hopes of seeing deer. At the far limit of the beam he saw a large animal, but very indistinctly. It was too light-colored for a bear. He noted the creature held its head low. It disappeared immediately without a sound. He wasn't sure what it was, or what it wasn't!

This period offered wonderful nights for canoeing.

The moon was full and flooded the north country with a rich silver glow. Nighthawks played about the stars, giving forth their weird wing sounds. We went paddling on the glassy waters every evening. To add to the joy of the experience, Loony Coon formed the habit of going along. The creature had good canoe manners. He seldom moved about, but sat in the very center of the craft looking out into the night and by his sensitive nostrils learning more of what was going on in the black woods than we could know. Sometimes when a stray woodland breeze brought him an exciting scent, he would rise high on his hind legs after the manner of a bear and sniff eagerly. Whether it was friend or foe whose olfactory message he intercepted, we could only guess.

One night Loony Coon became much agitated. We were paddling close to the shore near the Clearing. A little forest breeze set the leaves of shore-line aspens to dancing, but otherwise the north country was cloaked in stillness. The raccoon nervously walked back and forth in the canoe. He stood up and sniffed the air. Then he made a peculiar little grunting noise.

"Loony Coon, be still!" Giny said from her place on the bow seat. "Lie down. That is no way to behave in a canoe."

"Quiet, boy," I said.

Loony Coon had no notion of being quiet. He came to me in the stern, placed his front feet on my knee and rose up to look in my face as if he were trying to tell me something. Then he made the grunting noise again. We were quite close to shore by this time, and he looked eagerly into the dark forest.

"He detects something back in there, dear," I said to Giny in low voice. "I've never seen him so excited. He's trembling." Loony Coon now stood with his front paws on the side of the canoe, his whole attention directed into the dark vastness of the forest.

"Listen—something is running!" whispered Giny.

From far back in the night came the sound of hoofs. It grew louder. The creatures making it were coming our way rapidly.

"Deer!" I said excitedly. "Something has frightened them."

"But there has been no alarm snort," said Giny. "Don't they usually snort when they are frightened?"

"Yes, usually," I agreed. "Here they come. Maybe they need all their breath just to run."

We had no time for further speculation. The racing animals were right on us. Loony Coon made a dive under my seat and stayed there. Giny and I sprayed our flashlights in the direction of the onrushing animals. Suddenly a doe and two fawns flashed out of the forest right into the ray from our lights. Likely it was Bobette, Fiddlesticks and Freckles, but the action was too hectic for positive identification. There was no play in the scene before us, no humor. Obviously the animals were frightened to the point of desperation. In two magnificent bounds the doe crossed the narrow beach, and the fawns followed closely. Oblivious of our presence, they plunged into the water a few feet from our canoe and swam into the lake. With our flashlights we followed their three heads into the distance as they swam with all their strength. They passed beyond the range of visibility, but we could hear an occasional splash as a hoof would break water and by this traced their course to the far shore. Our lake at this point is only about an eighth of a mile wide, which is not a long swim for a deer.

Giny drew in a deep breath, the first one in five minutes, she said afterward. "What does all this mean!"

Loony Coon gave intermittent grunts and hovered close to my feet.

"Something out of the ordinary," I commented, puzzled. "Let's have a look ashore."

We beached our canoe and stepped out on the sands. Loony Coon refused to budge, but held his position under the seat. His nose sniffed frantically at the night air, and his grunts continued.

With our flashlights we worked our way through the trees to the Clearing. We played the rays about the open ground. Everything seemed as usual, but there was a strange, eerie feeling about the place. A whippoorwill began calling in the distance, and an osprey added his weird cry to the night.

"Sam," Giny whispered, "there's something moving the bushes over near the road." She guided my attention with the ray of her light. "Is the wind doing that?"

"Not unless a wind has found a way to blow in that spot and no other," I observed, actually trembling with excitement. "Something big is moving those alders."

We turned the flashlights this way and that. The bushes waved sharply, and we could trace the progress of some creature moving through them toward the heavier timber. Then all became quiet.

"Are we going over there?" asked Giny. There was anxiety in the question rather than the mere request for information.

I continued to search around with my light. "Oh, I believe not," I said, trying to sound casual.

Giny heaved a sigh of relief.

We didn't talk about it, but we sensed just a little fear of that something or other that was over in those dark forest chambers. The mystery of it, the silence, the desperate flight of the deer, the actions of Loony Coon, all served to challenge our confidence that the forest offered no danger to man.

"Of course, we know that cat wouldn't attack us," said Giny, striving to be reassuring.

"Yes," I agreed. Then I added, "But does *he* know it?"

I led the way back to the canoe at a pace that was a bit on the hurry-up side.

Loony Coon was still tucked away under the seat. He seemed relieved at our return, but continued to give his funny little grunts.

"Bobette was a wise old girl, taking to the water," I commented, as I slipped the canoe into the lake. "That's one thing a panther wouldn't like."

"If that was Bobette," Giny added.

"And if it is a panther," I said.

VI

ESCAPE FROM A WHOOPINGDINGER

GINY and I both had dreams based on our experience at the Clearing that night.

"Every time I closed my eyes I lived that scene again," I told her as we sat at breakfast the next morning. "I saw those three deer running madly, and what bothered me was that they seemed to make no progress. It was like running through deep water. Always I had the feeling that the thing chasing them was just one good bound behind."

"But didn't you get chased by a whoopingdinger?" she asked seriously.

"A whoopingdinger?"

"Yes—a real, live whopper of a whoopingdinger!" she said emphatically. "I did—and it was an ordeal, even in a dream."

"What did this whoopingdinger look like?" I asked.

"Just like all whoopingdingers," she said, persistently serious. "He was slightly larger than an elephant, but built like a cat. Yet he had horns, and his front feet were hands. He had stripes all over him and whiskers that dragged on the ground and a tail as long as a bull whip."

"You have been hearing and thinking too much about

a certain panther, supposed to be hereabouts." I laughed.

"My whoopingdinger came right out of the Clearing," Giny went on, refusing to be interrupted. "You

and I were in our canoe. Loony Coon was there too, and he could talk. He said, as plain as could be, 'I smell a whoopingdinger, and we better get out of here.' "

"Did we go?"

"Surely did, as fast as we could paddle. But the canoe acted as if it were dragging an anchor. We would stroke as hard as we could, and barely move an inch. Then ... then ..."

Giny served me with some griddlecakes.

"Go on," I insisted. "You have me all involved in your dream. Don't leave me there. What happened?"

"Then the whoopingdinger burst out of the woods right behind us," she said, widening her eyes. "I think there was smoke coming from his nostrils, but I couldn't be sure of that. And, strangely, *I* was at stern paddle, where he could get to me first. Don't you ever put me at stern paddle again when a whoopingdinger is coming, will you?"

She threatened to pour hot chocolate down my neck.

"No! No!" I yelled. "But what happened? Did he get us?"

"He followed us," she continued. "And the funny thing was, he could walk on the water. Loony Coon looked back at him and said, 'See, what did I tell you? My nose always knows.' He crawled under the seat and hid. That whoopingdinger gained on us at every jump. I could feel his hot breath on the back of my neck. And then . . ." She hesitated. "Tune in tomorrow at this same time, same station," she said, in change of mood, "and find out if the whoopingdinger got Sam and Giny."

"I won't stand for it," I cried, pushing my breakfast back and rising. "I want to know now. Did you grapple with the beast, best him in a hand-to-hand struggle, tear him limb from limb?"

"No," said Giny. "Why all the violence? I simply woke up on him. That's all. It was easy."

"Oh," I said, going back to my griddlecakes. "Glad you didn't stay in that dream—you would have had us both in serious trouble. I would like to have seen that whoopingdinger walking on the water, though."

"Likely he's still doing it back in that dream, wondering where we all went," Giny concluded. "And now let's stop our foolishness and get back to the Clearing. There may be some interesting tracks."

"Of the whoopingdinger?"

"Don't be silly—you can't make tracks in water, even when you walk on it."

We searched the Clearing well, but there were no tracks. At the shore line were the deep indentations where the deer had leaped for the water, but only their hoofmarks could be found. We studied the land about the alders where we had seen movement the night before, but the ground was covered with ferns, matted leaves and blueberry plants so there were no footprints of which we could be sure. The old roadway bore no record except of the visit of deer.

Giny and I separated and wandered about for a few minutes, searching for any helpful evidence.

Presently she called me. "Come see what you make of these markings on this tree," she said.

When I reached her she pointed out a place on the trunk of a cedar tree some seven feet from the ground where the bark was ruffled up.

"See, the scar looks as if it may have been made with claws," she observed. "There are scratches running downward. Maybe I have a cat complex, but it looks like the mark I have seen domestic cats make, sometimes on furniture, when they stretch and scratch."

"Yes," I agreed, looking at the marks. "That's a possible interpretation. But a bear could do that too."

"Reaching that high?"

"Yes, a five-hundred-pound bear could easily reach that high."

We studied the ground at the base of the tree, but it was grassy and bore no marking that was helpful.

"Oh, when *are* we going to know for sure whether this is a panther?" said Giny a bit impatiently. "Our evidence is always so inconclusive. Everything we see says it could be, but we can't be sure."

"That's nature for you," I replied, still looking at the marks on the tree. "She knows you value your facts more if you have to work hard for them. We'll get final word someday, likely when we least expect it."

Bobette and her fawns did not come to the Clearing that morning. The place seemed lonely and empty without them. In fact, we did not see a living creature, not even a rabbit.

There was a development in the nest of our song sparrow that was unpleasant. One sparrow egg had been discarded or forced from the nest, and there remained the one large cowbird egg, and the other one of the sparrow. The little mother bird was reluctant to leave the nest, and we knew that hatching time was drawing near.

We could only speculate on what had happened to the one egg. The shell was on the ground beneath the nest, right where it had fallen. Had it been pushed out accidentally by the mother bird? This seemed unlikely, for such creatures are careful and efficient about their nest homes. Was it infertile and had this bird some way of knowing, so that she deliberately destroyed it?

"Could it be that the cowbird who placed the egg in the nest eliminated that egg so that her young one would have better living conditions?" Giny questioned. "Does such a cowbird keep in contact with the nest housing her egg?"

"I believe the answers to your questions aren't known as yet," I replied. "I've never heard of anyone who has had opportunity to watch the whole cycle of this cowbird rearing plan."

"Well," Giny said, looking at the eggshell on the ground, "if that cowbird actually pushed that egg out she ought to be spanked."

We found a spot from which we could see the nest clearly through binoculars without disturbing the songbird. Constant observation was going to be necessary if we were to learn anything about this diminutive drama of the forest. A schedule was arranged so that every few hours one of us examined the nest, carefully watching for any change that might be taking place.

One evening, while twilight still reigned, we followed the old trail to Vanishing Lake. This lovely little body of water lies nearly a mile back in the forest. The Clearing had demanded so much of our attention this season that we neglected this favorite haunt, where through the years we had so many valuable nature adventures. Loony Coon rode in the canoe to the mainland, and to our surprise followed us down the trail.

"You funny old thing," Giny said, patting him, "I don't believe you know you are a raccoon. Maybe you think you're a puppy, following us around like this."

Loony Coon reached his head high to take some petting and then ran along the trail in his odd, half-sideways lope.

We heard the evening bird chorus, always so prominent at Vanishing Lake. The sharpest voice of all was that of the ovenbird, who screamed "Teacher, teacher, teacher," endlessly. The red-eyed vireo, aptly called the "preacher bird" was expounding his sermon monotonously, slowly putting the forest to sleep. From the leafy bowers overhead came the spiral song of the olive-backed thrush, and somewhere in the distance a wood thrush was singing his dual tones.

Near the lake came one of those experiences that make life in the forest so continuously interesting. We sighted a red fox on a hillside, his color emphasized by the evening light. The fox is a notably shy creature, and I called on Giny to look quickly before he fled. But he did not flee. Instead, he sat down and stared at us.

"Could it be Zowie?" Giny asked anxiously, mentioning a fox we had as a pet several years previously.

"Could be," I replied, "and I hope it is. I liked Zowie and I miss him."

Foxes make intimate and affectionate pets when they are young but they take quickly to the wilds. Never have we had one stay with us beyond the first year. By nature they are hunters and wanderers, and the call of the wilderness is strong in their hearts.

"A wild fox wouldn't do that," Giny insisted. She called to the creature and coaxed him to come to us. He didn't come, but he didn't run away either. Presently he trotted a few feet and then sat down again. As he did, we got a full look at him.

"What a beautiful creature!" Giny exclaimed. "His coat and his tail are so thick and lovely. It must be Zowie."

"Or one of the other foxes we have had," I said. "As you say, no wild fox would behave like that."

Before the animal disappeared into the brush, he gave a short little bark. A moment later he reappeared at a point higher up the hill, and paused to look back at us again. Then he went on into his green mansion to live life as he likes it best.

Suddenly Giny grasped my arm and directed my attention to the summit of the hill. A forest fire had once swept this knoll and left it barren except for several high white pines that survived the flames. There, silhouetted against the sky, I discovered the figures of three deer. One was a doe that moved along sedately, pausing occasionally to browse on leaves of young maples. The other two were fawns—one of whom walked with head erect and steps that savored of a strut!

"Fiddlesticks!" cried Giny. "Bobette, Freckles, is this where you went?"

The deer paused, looking at us with ears forward. As we both continued to call, they walked toward us. There was no question as to their identity. This was our family from the Clearing.

"Did that old thing, whatever it is, chase you away from your home, pets?" Giny questioned. We started toward them and they awaited our coming.

"Wise old Bobette," I said admiringly. "The Clearing has become a dangerous place for her family so she moved here."

"But there are wolves and coyotes in this area," said Giny.

"Yes, but the hazard at the Clearing is the greater one. I believe she has the wisdom to meet every situation. She is going to bring Fiddlesticks and Freckles through."

"Well, at least she doesn't have to face a whoopingdinger," said Giny consolingly.

The three creatures waited until we were within a few feet of them, and then, having met the demands of social courtesy, walked to the hilltop. There Fiddlesticks struck one of his best statuelike poses, as though he were conscious of his high position and wanted to give an admiring world something to look at. Freckles stood looking at him as if in awe of his lordly grandeur. Bobette failed to be impressed. She walked to him and by way of reminding him that he was still only a speckled fawn, an upstart in the forest world, she washed his neck and ears. Then she gave him a playful nudge with her nose as much as to say, "Down from your high horse, small fry; you're not dry behind the ears yet."

"It takes a mother to do that," I commented, remembering comparable experiences of my own.

VII

THE VOICE OF THE WILD

WE KEPT Moke informed of events at our Sanctuary. He became our best news customer. We felt each new happening was incomplete until we had written of it to Moke. His scribbled replies were not always intended for Giny and me. One letter was to Bobette. It contained much advice on how to cope with the panther, so Liliana's interpretation told us. He told her just to dig a big hole and run in there whenever the *popoki nui* (the big cat) came near. Moke knew about cats. His cousin had one. He sent instructions to Giny and me to put a bell on *Popoki Nui's* neck. His cousin did, and that warned the birds when that cat approached them. This bell on our panther would help Bobette, Fiddlesticks and Freckles escape, he was sure.

"You have no idea what a hero you have become to my Moke," Giny read aloud from one of Liliana's letters. "He talks of you and your animals constantly. I permit him to call you 'Sam and Giny,' or to attempt to do so, but the best his tongue can do sounds like 'Kam and Geenee.' I hope you do not mind. You are helping with his first arithmetic, for he is learning to count the months until you come. I wish you could see him when

73

one of your letters arrives. His happiness knows no bounds and I have no peace until I read it to him."

Giny read the next few lines to herself, casting an occasional side glance at me.

"Is there something personal in there?" I questioned. "May I not hear the rest?"

"I'm not sure—it may not be good for you," she said, glaring at me. "This might make you strut around like Fiddlesticks."

"Now, I must have it!" I declared, all attention.

"Well, here it comes," said Giny resignedly, "but against my better judgment."

"Moke meets the postman every day," Giny read on. "If there is one of your envelopes, he comes carrying it to me as if it were a priceless but breakable treasure. I must open it in a certain way. With a pair of shears I cut a thin strip off the end, but under penalties like those of the taboo system I dare not open the flap. This restriction went on for a while with no explanation. Then one day I pinned him down. 'Moke, why can't I open the flap, as I do with other letters?' It is rather hard to tell you his answer delicately. I feel inclined to say that it was because you had sealed the envelope, and that made it precious to him. But what he really said was, 'Oh—Kam spit on that place!' "

Giny put down the letter and glared at me, watching apprehensively the effect of this flattery. In spite of her assumed concern and severity, laughter was breaking through everywhere. I rose to my feet, expanded my chest, and walked stiffly across the room. "Fiddlesticks," I said, looking out the window, "move over. Here I come!"

Moke's letters were not the only ones we received, though he was the youngest and most persistent of our correspondents. Other young people who had walked across the Sanctuary scene and found their way into my books kept us posted as to their activities. Little Kona, the Indian boy of Arizona, was able to write his own letters and sent us joyful accounts of his daily experiences that indicated he was living a happy life. Hi-Bub, who had contributed so much to our experience through his boyhood and youth, had completed his first year in college. With his parents he was going west to see the Canadian Rockies. Sonya, the little girl who had to teach her mother to love animals, was going with her family on a visit to Africa. In her letter she promised to bring us a pet elephant. Sandy, the fine young woodsman with whom we had made journeys into the Canadian canoe wilderness, wrote us from Alaska, where he was carrying out a nature project.

"Grand youngsters," Giny affirmed, as we sat talking of these treasured young friends. "How much they have given us!"

"They have," I agreed. "And now comes Moke with his little arms loaded with blessings. He is going to write another rich chapter in our lives."

"Yes, bless his heart," she said, then her mood changed sharply. "But if you even mention that envelope incident, I won't bake a blueberry pie for you all summer."

Under that threat I curtailed my egotism, but it wasn't easy.

We saw Bobette and her family several times in the Vanishing Lake area. Once at dawn we looked out from the trail toward the little lake, and saw the three of them drinking. Bobette's training of her youngsters was in evidence. All partook plentifully of the water, but never did all three drink at once. One was always on guard. Two heads would be down, and one would be up. The watcher looked alertly at the shores and the hilltop and sniffed at the forest breeze. There must never be a careless moment in their lives, never an instant when they are off guard. Eternal vigilance is their unvoiced motto.

We saw Bobette schooling her twins in other elements of defense. She led them through the forest at high speed, by example teaching them to jump over logs and brush. She entered their games of tag, and raced about with them in apparent play, but every move was teaching them something vital to their very existence. We saw her sparring with them, rising on her hind feet and striking at them with her forefeet. Her blows were strong enough that the fawns did not want them to land,

and they struck back at her. This defensive move must be learned in a very practical way. The time would come when these fawns would be adult deer, and Bobette no longer near to direct and defend them. They might be attacked by wolves or coyotes. Then these blows of the front feet, delivered accurately and forcefully, could defeat even these age-old enemies. While the two fawns were still nurslings, Bobette was introducing them to the leaves, grasses, mosses and mushrooms that would be their ultimate diet. She taught them to wade into the water, there to get the tender leaves of water lilies, and to lick the natural mineral deposit at certain rocks and roots of trees. Her task of training these two was a big responsibility which she did not shirk for a moment.

We kept watch of the roads and the lake-shore sands for any tracks of our big cat. For days there was not a single bit of evidence pointing to his presence. Rabbits came back into the Clearing, and the forest seemed mild and calm once more.

Then came that evening Giny and I will never forget. It was one of those silent nights which true nature students prize so highly. The whole forest world settled into a mood of mixed peace and expectancy. Not a breeze stirred the pine needles, not a frog called, and even the insects were quiet. Caught up in the mood, Giny and I sculled our canoe along, so that even the dripping of paddles would not break the stillness.

We moved along the shore where the trail to Vanishing Lake begins. Across the north horizon a low ring of northern lights graced the sky, and the rugged silhouettes of white pines stood out boldly against the glow. Venus, the evening star, shown like a lantern in the east. Meteors occasionally wrote their fading messages through the field of the stars.

We ceased our paddling and let the canoe drift. The silence reached its supreme climax, and we drank it deeply into our hearts. Then came a cry out of the darkness that no man on earth can listen to stoically. I have heard it previously in the mountains of the west. It began in a low but strong tone, then rose in volume and pitch until it seemed to fill the forest.

The sound defies description. It is the wildest cry of the alley cat multiplied a hundredfold. My scalp tingled with a sense of fear that all my experience in the forest could not curtail. Giny gasped. There was no mistaking what we heard. No longer did we lack for concrete evidence of what that forest contained. This was the cry of the panther. Pioneers likened it to the desperate shrieks of a woman in distress. The very ferocity of the cry led to the exaggerated stories that were written in pioneer days—of men carried away by the animal, of fierce attacks that would destroy a whole household, and of supernatural powers that this beast was supposed to possess.

At that moment the feeling of primitive wilderness

returned to the north country. The cry erased from our thoughts realization that along these shores were modern cabins, with up-to-date electrical equipment and conveniences, that there were people within a few min-

utes' paddle of where we floated on the water. The whole world seemed one vast primeval forest and we the only people in it. The cry came back to us again as it echoed from the shore to the north, and again from the sides of Brown Hill. Then it died away, leaving the forest in deeper silence than before.

"That was he?" Giny asked, when she could find her voice.

"That was he!" I affirmed. There seemed nothing more to say.

VIII

ADVENTURE AT PANTHER PALACE

THERE was little sleeping done that night at the Campbell cabin. We lay awake, half hoping, half fearing that we would hear the cry of the panther again. It was not repeated that night, but the one call we had heard echoed and re-echoed in our thoughts.

"That cry came from the vicinity of Vanishing Lake, didn't it?" asked Giny.

"Yes, it was in that general direction."

"Right where Bobette and the fawns are," Giny meditated apprehensively. "If only we could get them to our island!"

I was silent. This wish had been present with me, too, but I saw no way to accomplish it.

Near morning, when the first gray light was playing low on the eastern horizon, I heard the occasional splash of a large animal swimming the lake. It was too far away from our island to be identified. I wondered if it could be our deer family, once more escaping the panther by means of water.

Perhaps it was, for the next morning we found the three deer in the Clearing. Their mood was quite different from that prevailing when we saw them at Vanishing Lake. There was no play in them, and Fiddlesticks and Freckles held closely to their mother. Bobette bent her head to the ground only long enough to get a mouthful of chosen green food, and then straightened up to watch the margins of the Clearing vigilantly as she completed the chewing process. She gave little attention to us though we approached rather closely.

Giny and I were most desirous of seeing the panther. Now that we were sure of his identity and the unwarranted fear produced by his cry had subsided, we wanted a look at the creature.

Once in earlier years during my forest wanderings I had come upon a place where two large glacier boulders had lodged together, forming a sort of cave. The thought of this place haunted me. What an ideal home for our panther!

"Maybe it's intuition," I said to Giny. "I can't get that place out of my mind. Why, it would be ideal for the big cat! He would be searching for such a spot, and caves and rock shelters are scarce in this country. It could be that the old boy, if he is a boy, is right there."

"Where is this perfect kitty palace?" she asked.

"I am not sure, it has been so many years since I saw it, but I believe it was in that hill country northwest of Somewhere Lake."

"All right," she said, always ready for an adventure. "Wind up your intuition and let's go. If that cat is there, we can probably hear him purring half a mile away."

Carrying some light-weight camera equipment and

some emergency rations in a packsack, we made an all-day trip in search of Panther Palace as we called it. The country we went into was rough. There had been a logging operation since my earlier visit, and the brushy debris lay crisscrossed and tangled. We climbed, and tripped, and stumbled most of the day. The only rewarding feature was the sight of a black bear who was bathing in a creek. He looked up at us in amazement that anyone of our kind would invade his domain. Then he gave a grunt of unwelcome, and disappeared into a thicket.

The threat of darkness catching us in this land led us to turn back in late afternoon and start for home. Suddenly, right before us, stood the two great boulders and the resultant cave beneath.

"That's it!" I exclaimed.

"Wonderful," said Giny. Both of us spoke in soft tones. "That's a perfect panther home. Do you suppose he's in there now?"

"Let's be as quiet as we can," I suggested. "We'll soon find out."

Being quiet in such a woods is not easy, and there was many a twig that cracked as we crept forward.

"Do you mean to crawl right into the thing?" asked Giny, tugging at my sleeve. "Let's just watch from here—this is close enough."

The cave did look close and it yawned as if it wanted to swallow us up. I was thinking of the cry we had heard at Vanishing Lake, and no doubt Giny was too.

"Sh-h-h-h," I whispered. "I hear something moving up inside the cave."

Sure enough, there was a rustle of dry leaves in the dark depths before us. We were too excited to appraise the sounds properly, but unquestionably there was something alive under those rocks.

The rustle in the leaves grew stronger. "It's coming this way," I whispered. "See if you can get the camera out of the packsack."

"Isn't it too dark for a picture?" she asked.

"It may be, but let's try."

"Yes, but who's going to hold that camera steady?" Giny asked. The way her hands were shaking, the picture would look as if it were taken in an earthquake.

We were crouched behind an alder bush, peering out at the cave entrance. I found my hands were behaving about the same way, so I held the camera against the side of a small tree to steady it. The rustling was closer now.

"He's coming out," Giny said in a whisper that was almost a shout. "Get ready."

"I-I-I-I yam r-r-r-r-ready," I said, and then to bolster up my own courage I added, "Come, kitty, come, kitty, come, kitty."

The rustling sounds reached a climax, and so did our excitement. Suddenly the creature came. With a magnificent bound he cleared the cave entrance—and

perched on a small broken branch of a birch tree. There before us sat the beast, *Tamias striatus*—a common old chipmunk.

Giny looked at me and I looked at her and *Tamias striatus* looked at both of us. His expression seemed to say, "What's the matter, folks, didn't you expect me?" Then we broke into loud laughter, and our chipmunk went chirping resentfully into a brush pile. We looked back into our cave with a flashlight. It was quite shallow, and all we found was an earthworm and the crumbs of a pine cone where a squirrel had eaten his dinner.

"I have a suggestion," I said, breaking a long silence as we made our way home.

"Yes?"

"Let's not tell our friends about our hair-raising adventure at Panther Palace."

"Agreed," said Giny. "And I have a suggestion too."

"Yes?"

"Let's change the name of the place to Chipmunk Chalet."

IX

BING, BOOM AND DOUBLE TROUBLE

OUR SEARCH for a sight of the great cat continued daily. We found his tracks near Vanishing Lake and again along the bank of the little creek that flows into the west bay of our lake. Once more we heard his cry, coming as before when we were canoeing in the night. It affected us much as it had the first time we heard it.

A note from Moke suggested we give the big cat (*popoki nui*) a saucer of milk, and furthermore he thought it ought to be warmed!

"No doubt Popoki Nui would eat it," I said to Giny.

"Yes, and the saucer too."

We found we were adopting Moke's name for the panther. Popoki or Popoki Nui was much more individual than just "the big cat" or "the panther."

Moke's note, interpreted by his mother's accompanying letter, bore a message of concern. Ewa the chicken was getting mean to Kimo the mongoose. "We expected this to go the other way," ran the letter. "Ewa is boss and she pecks Kimo on the nose if he doesn't do just as she wants him to. Kimo submits to it meekly and does not retaliate. They are really cute and often go walking together. When Ewa has been mean to Kimo, he comes to us for sympathy. He makes a funny little squeaking noise, apparently grumbling about his treatment, and we have to pet and console him. We fear Ewa is the only chicken that commands his respect, however. Our neighbor has lost several chickens and once I saw a feather on Kimo's nose. It is only circumstantial evidence, but it looks suspicious. We are trying so hard to keep the Kimo-Ewa romance going until you arrive—but I wonder. By the way, it is only five months now. Moke has enough fingers on one hand to count the time until you come. He thinks the little finger must be a short month and that helps hurry the great event along."

In the song-sparrow nest things were happening that took our thoughts off Popoki Nui some of the time. The smaller of the two eggs hatched first and into the world came a funny-looking little thing that would someday be a song sparrow. We called him "Bing" partly because he was a little outburst and partly because he would be a singer someday. When the larger egg hatched and a clumsy, awkward, yapping cowbird began his earthly existence, we named him "Boom."

It didn't take Bing and Boom long to get started on their job of being tiny birds. They stretched their mouths wide, begging food of the song-sparrow parents—just a couple of thinly feathered bottomless pits. There was very little song-sparrow singing done those first few days. The task of gathering insects and ramming them into those begging beaks demanded all their attention and breath. Boom looked almost as large as

his foster parents to start with. When he opened his mouth it seemed the song-sparrow mother might fall right in.

Boom did a lot of wriggling around. He crowded Bing and made him feel mighty unwelcome in his own home. We watched this closely, for it is not unusual for these uninvited stepchildren to force the legitimate heirs out on the ground. However, Bing nestled down to the bottom of the nest and seemed able to hold his own. Our observations convinced us that he got as much food as Boom, so we concluded that everything was going as smoothly as could be expected in this household—so far!

There came a day when we had not a chance to think of Boom and Bing, nor Popoki Nui either. We did not plan it that way. In fact, it was our design for the day that we take a picnic lunch and wander all day long in new areas searching for a sight of our panther.

Right at dawn the unwelcome old woodpecker beat a reveille on the downspout. *Rat-ta-tat-tat, rat-ta-tat-tat,* he went. His mood was most persistent that morning. Several times he returned to his drumming.

Sleepily I rolled out of bed. "I wish that scoundrel had to do his pecking on the North Pole," I growled. "If I get my hands on him I'll give him a good start in that direction. I'll——"

"Sh-h-h-h-h," said Giny. "There's a new sound outside. What is it?"

From near the front door came a low-pitched whine. Still half asleep, I tried to conclude it came from Loony Coon, or perhaps the woodchuck, but it didn't fit with either. The sound came again, a bit stronger this time. Then a second voice joined, and we had a pair of whines. We dressed hurriedly. Giny reached the front door first and looked out. A quick gasp escaped her. "Oh, you beautiful things!" she exclaimed.

I was beside her in an instant, in turn gasping and looking in admiration at those "beautiful things." There stood two huge, lovely-to-look-at Irish setters. They were so nearly alike that I rubbed my eyes, wondering if I was seeing double. But there were still two of them when I looked again. They stood side by side, heads pitched at the same angle, and even their tails wagged in unison. Their expressions were a study. I never saw a thought more clearly portrayed without a word being spoken. Within them was an intense anticipation and yearning which found outlet in their eyes, their half-open mouths, their excited breathing. With all their being they were asking for help and friendship, and perhaps a few dog biscuits thrown in.

"Where did you come from?" Giny was questioning. "And what brings you to our island? Where are you going?"

Obviously they had just landed on the island, for their hair was dripping from their swim.

"They must be hungry!" Giny exclaimed. "I'll get them some scraps." She hurried to the kitchen.

I promptly made a mistake. I went out to meet our guests and to pet those red-brown heads and backs. How they grasped at that affection! They wagged their big tails until I feared they would break off. They pushed against me, licked my hands and whined and whined in pure delight.

Then, as if by agreement, they both rose simultaneously (standing as tall as I) and placed their front feet against me—*forcefully*. Stepping back at the impact, I tripped on a root and fell to the ground This, from their doggy viewpoint, was exactly what was wanted. "*Arf, arf,*" they barked, apparently saying that this new friend was a good fellow—he would come down to their level. With some such thought they pounced on me, holding me to the ground, licking my face, ears, and hair with unstinted enthusiasm and tireless tongues. It seemed to me there were twice as many legs stepping on me as could possibly belong to just two dogs, and they

were more of the size and quality one would expect to find on a horse.

"Fido, Fifi, Sport," I cried, vainly, trying every dog name I could think of. "Charge, lie down, go fetch, to heel—do something or go some place."

My commands had no effect except to increase their enthusiasm. They became playful in the extreme. One took a mouthful of my shirt and started north, while the other took an equally big bite of my breeches and headed south. I was suspended somewhere in between.

No doubt I would have been partly disrobed, if not

dismembered, had not Giny appeared on the scene, carrying two pans heaping with food. Taking no notice of my situation, she said: "You poor creatures! Sam—stop being rough with them, they're hungry. Here...."

The pans were placed before them, and the food disappeared as if by magic. The pans were filled again and emptied the same way. While a third serving was being prepared, likely involving things planned for our own dinner that day, I went in and washed the canine caresses off my face. I also put on a stronger shirt and tougher breeches. No telling what this day was going to bring forth.

When I returned to the scene of the banquet-riot, the two dogs were sitting quietly side by side and Giny was petting them. I doubt if they were filled. I believe nothing could fill them. More likely they were just tired of eating and needed a rest.

Now we could see that there was quite a difference in the ages of the two dogs. One was an overgrown puppy, while the other was probably his mother. I saw too that I was not the only victim of their invasion. Hearing a scratching noise in a tall white pine, I looked up to see six raccoons, including Loony Coon, who had headed aloft when our guests arrived. Patty Sausage, the saucy woodchuck, was peeking out of her hole in the ground, saying some impolite and uncomplimentary things to the dogs in low, growling tones. Whatever Patty left unsaid was voiced by our chipmunks and red squirrels from safe positions in the brush and trees. It was all wasted on our visitors. They just sat and looked up at us, saying with their eyes, "What do we do now?"

We were asking the question of each other too. "What *shall* we do?" Giny asked, still stroking the willing heads. "These creatures are pets. They aren't just stray dogs. Someone is worried about them and seeking them."

"Never saw dogs like them in this region," I commented. "It may be that their masters are just summer visitors up here, and the dogs, not used to the woods, wandered away."

"Well, suppose we take them in the boat and call at the cabins along the lake shores," Giny suggested.

It was a good idea, but getting the dogs into the boat was something else again. The older setter went in at once, seeming to understand what the plan was, but the overgrown pup started to whimper the moment he got near the boat. On the pier he lay flat down and refused to budge. His attitude was pathetic. One would have thought he was being beaten with a whip. He whined and trembled. We coaxed and pleaded and tried to bribe him with bites of Giny's delicious cookies. He took our offering but he didn't get into the boat. I tried spanking him, but he just licked my hand, and I felt like a size 18 heel.

The mother dog was not so tenderhearted. She watched our futile efforts from her position in the boat, growling out some orders to the frightened and stubborn youngster. When she saw that our efforts had failed, and Giny and I stood back discouraged and frustrated, she made a graceful leap out of the boat and pounced on the pup. She went at him as if she meant to eat him alive, growling, snarling and biting viciously—at least to appearances. The younger dog yiped as if he were being murdered, but he ended in the boat just the same. He curled up on a seat and the mother sat beside him, looking up at us as if saying, "That's what it takes. You just never raised any children and you don't know. Sometimes you have to be firm."

Down the lake shores we went in our outboard motorboat, running from pier to pier. I watched the mother dog as we approached each place, for I was sure she would recognize her home and give some signs. But she just held her position and looked at us constantly as if trying to tell us something.

Everywhere we went the dogs were petted and admired, but no one owned them. We did get a thread of a story we could piece together. At one cabin to the south of us they had appeared two nights previously. These people fed them. The next day the dogs disappeared. We heard from the mailman that two such dogs had stopped at a farm still farther south several days back and they had spent one night at a backwoods grocery store prior to that. Apparently they were heading north, panhandling as they went.

Failing to find an owner along the lake shore, we went to the landing where we kept our car. There was no trouble with the dogs here. They both climbed into the back seat and sat down; apparently a car was something they were accustomed to.

Then we drove to town to make inquiry. No one knew anything about the dogs, though several wanted to adopt them. We couldn't permit that. Whoever owned these lovely creatures would be grieving for them, and we wanted to see them at their real home.

The search continued on through the day. We went to stores, garages, service stations, post offices; we telephoned far and wide. Still no leads. The dogs became hungry. So did we. Then I made the horrible discovery that in changing clothes I had left my money at home. I had to suffer the embarrassment of telling this story to the owner of a roadside sandwich stand, begging credit. With a look on his face that said, "I've heard everything now," he reluctantly made sandwiches for us all. The dogs ate theirs at the rate of one gulp per half sandwich.

"I'll see you later," I called to the man as we left, feeling as guilty as he thought I was.

"Mebbe" was his reply.

Our course led us to the north. From what we had learned, that was the way the dogs were traveling and I have implicit faith in the homing instinct of such creatures.

Toward the end of the day we had a lead. At a grocery store back in the woods the owner said he knew two such dogs. A man had come to his store occasionally that summer with the dogs in the rear seat of his car. He knew where this man lived and the kind of a car he drove. "Might come in this afternoon," he said. "He usually does—though sometimes he skips a day."

We decided this might be one of the days the man skipped, so we got directions and started for his cabin. It was far out on a winding forest road. When we got on this lane, the dogs showed some anxiety. This became almost violent when a car came in sight. The younger dog came right over my shoulder and grabbed for my steering wheel. The mother thought this was an impolite move which called for discipline, so she started a fight with her offspring right on the back of my neck. I managed to get the car stopped, and the approaching one halted too. The dogs were trying to get out the windshield. When I did manage to get the door open, the two creatures staged a Hollywood mob scene right across my head, taking special care to tromp on my ears with their big feet.

Several people emerged from the other car, and the two exuberant creatures went bounding to meet them. The reunion was touching to see. Unquestionably these were the owners of our dogs. The people gathered about the dogs, alternately scolding them for being lost and praising them for coming back. The dogs wiggled their terrible tails all the way from their noses back to the ends.

These were lovely people and we were grateful for the circumstance that led us to know them. There were a father, mother, and two teen-aged daughters. The girls were in tears at the return of their pets. The father offered us any cash reward that we would accept.

"No—" I laughed—"we are overpaid now. I don't know when we have had so much fun in a single day. There is one thing you can do for me, if you will."

"What is it?"

"Lend me some money, with the privilege of sending you a check in repayment tomorrow," I said, blushing with embarrassment. I told him how we had obtained sandwiches from the wayside stand. Cheerfully he gave me the money.

We studied a map of the region which the man had in his car. Checking on it the places where the dogs had stayed and the position of our cabin relative to his, we saw that the animals had been headed straight toward his place. The farthest point from home they had reached of which we knew was forty miles to the south.

"They began chasing deer," he said, looking at the dogs reproachfully. "We tried to break them, but they kept on. Then they disappeared, we suppose on one of these chases. We searched for them but did not find a trace. I nearly left the road when I saw them in your car."

We left our new friends, carrying an invitation to come back and see them—and the two dogs.

On the way home we stopped to pay our bill at the sandwich stand. The owner fingered the money I gave him, looking at me thoughtfully. "Wish you hadn't done this," he said.

"Why?"

"Restores my faith in human nature, and I don't like it," he said with a shake of his head. "Bet it'll cost me a hundred before I get skeptical again. Wish you had never come back, then I'd *know* I never ought to trust a stranger."

It was evening when we got back to the island. The grounds were simply crawling with raccoons. They met us at the pier, reaching their front feet toward us as we glided the boat alongside. We gave them a ration of peanuts from the supply we carry in our pockets just for such emergencies. Then they trailed us to the cabin where we gave them a more abundant supply of food.

"This day has seemed a month long," Giny said, dropping into a chair. "Could it be that it was only this morning that those dogs came?"

"I know just how you feel," I replied. "It seems to me we have been gone so long the cabin looks strange."

Giny wasn't hearing me. She looked out a window through which our cabin lights were shining and her eyes widened with surprise at what she saw. I followed her gaze. There stood our two fawns, Fiddlesticks and

Freckles, looking in at us, and in the background, dimly outlined, was Bobette.

"Bless them!" Giny exclaimed. "They swam to our island. Oh, what made them do that?"

"Popoki Nui must be afoot," I said.

We contented ourselves with admiring them through the glass, fearing that we might frighten them back into the land of dangers if we went out.

X

SEEING IS BELIEVING

THE OLD woodpecker didn't need to awaken us the next morning. We were already dressed and outside our cabin when he came. He actually acted disappointed that he couldn't have the pleasure of disturbing us. Giving the metal pipe a single short *rat-tat*, he flew away uttering an unmusical nasal cry.

We were anxious to know if the deer were still on the island. Searching, we found them at the farthest point from the cabin. Possibly feeling themselves to be cornered, they acted nervous as we drew near and moved as if to swim away.

"Let's go no closer," Giny pleaded. "We do want them to stay. How wonderful if they would—they're safe here."

"Safe, but confined," I replied as we retreated toward the cabin. "That's something a wild creature does not like. The island is so small I doubt if they can be kept here long."

"Anyway, let's try!"

We did try. Our only hope was in finding some sort of food that appealed to them and which the forest did not offer. Once, in her younger years, Bobette had been very fond of potato chips. We had several packages of

101

these on hand. Moving cautiously we placed some of them on a log near the animals. Then we drew back to watch. For a long time the offering remained unnoticed. Freckles was lying down, Fiddlesticks was pestering his mother, and Bobette fed occasionally on maple leaves. Later Bobette made her way toward the log.

"Look, she's found them!" said Giny, much pleased.

Bobette came up to the log and sniffed at the potato chips. However, she gave them not so much as a lick before returning to her maple leaves. Fiddlesticks sniffed too—then, like the little wretch that he is, he pawed them off the log into the dirt and strutted away.

"Oh, Fiddlesticks," Giny complained, "why couldn't you like them? They have salt and everything."

"Maybe something sweet would please them," I suggested.

I shouldn't have said that. Giny rushed back to the cabin and returned with some pieces of a cake she had baked for me. With some resentment, I watched her place them on the log.

As it would take time for them to discover the new offering, we went in the cabin for our own breakfast. When we returned to observe the deer, the cake was gone.

"They liked it!" Giny exclaimed. Into the cabin she rushed to bring out the rest of what had been *my* cake. She put it on the same log and we retreated to a point from which we could watch it. The deer were moving about, quite unmindful of what we were doing. They walked down to the water and waded along the shore, Bobette eying the mainland.

"Are they going?" asked Giny.

"I believe they will not swim away in full daylight," I replied.

"What can we do to keep them? I'll bake cake for them all day long if that will make them stay."

I was looking back in the direction of the log on which the second serving of cake had been placed. I saw a dark-gray creature approaching the place.

"There is where your cake went!" I said with a forced smile.

"Loony Coon—oh, you rascal. Then the deer didn't get any after all."

Loony Coon it was. Famous for his appetite for cake, he made short work of this portion. Likely he had consumed the first one. Giny groaned.

We tried other things. A pan of milk sweetened with honey was placed in the deer area. Freckles tasted it, then walked away. Fiddlesticks walked up to it, stepped on the side of the pan and spilled the contents all over the ground. He never even looked down. An offering of bread was totally ignored, and finally went to Loony Coon. Cracked corn received some attention but drew no real enthusiasm.

Feeling frustrated, we went about other work. While I split wood, Giny put some things to wash. Presently she had a number of sheets on the line, waving moderately in the wind.

Fiddlesticks and Freckles now staged one of their races that circled the island. When they came in sight of the sheets they halted abruptly. This was something new and they were both fascinated and frightened. When the sheets gave a little extra flap in their direction, they disappeared into the bushes. Since the things didn't chase them, they came back to look at them again. Gathering courage, Fiddlesticks began advancing toward them while Freckles looked on in adoration. Here was hero worship at its best. Looking as if he would much rather not do it but couldn't turn back now, the strutting fawn moved a step at a time toward this great white mystery. He came so close he touched one of them with his nose. It didn't bite him. In fact it felt soft and gentle, so he pushed it about with his head. Then came one of those sudden gusts of wind. The sheet whipped about and spanked Fiddlesticks on his beautiful, spotted back. He rared up in the air and desperately pawed at the thing, in the manner Bobette had taught him. One leg got over the line, which broke with a snap, wrapping sheets all around Fiddlesticks. Bleating, he made a blind dash for liberty. Freckles was already gone. Sheets, pillowcases and other articles were dragged about over the ground before Fiddlesticks was free to dash to the far side of the island and tell Bobette all about it.

Giny and I watched the show with mixed emotions.

"Is someone going to do another washing?" I asked.

Giny flashed a glance at me that said plenty, and we both gathered up the bedraggled laundry.

An hour later I looked out the window from my desk. What I saw caused me to call Giny. "Look, the problem is solved," I said. "They have found something on the island to their liking, and I'm sure they cannot find it elsewhere."

Giny looked out the window, and then groaned. There was Fiddlesticks right in the midst of her flower garden! He ate the four lilies of the valley, the two tulips and the phlox. Apparently he didn't like the trilliums, so he stepped on those.

The next day Bobette and her two fawns were still on the island, much to our satisfaction. We had to go to a distant town for some photographic supplies. There was adventure for us along the road that day.

Our route led us over a busy highway. Cars were speeding by us all too fast, after the regrettable habit of the age. On forest roads particularly the speed of automobiles should be curtailed, for the safety of the drivers as well as the animals. Wild creatures have no way of coping with this danger. We counted on the roadside the remains of several birds, a porcupine, a raccoon and two woodchucks who could not get out of the way in time.

Ever since we had definitely established the fact that we really had a panther in our forest, I was picturing in my imagination the circumstances under which I would see him. Surely it would have to be at such a time and such a place as would give the ultimate in a wilderness experience. Likely it would be in some remote part of the forest, I thought, where men seldom if ever went. Perhaps it would be in the middle of the night when the mystery of the woods is greatest—or in the very early dawn. I fancied the great creature standing high on a rock looking about the forest, or perhaps perched in a tree, or emerging from a cave. The experience would give me a never-to-be-forgotten thrill.

Alas, for my dreams! They burst like a bubble before crass realism. Giny and I had barely begun our drive on the busy highway when the startling thing happened. Two cars had just passed us at high speed, and were still in sight. Right then and there, of all times and places, *a panther chose to show himself!* The great creature emerged from the brush at one side of the road and calmly trotted to the center. I put on my brakes and brought our car to a stop so suddenly Giny finished against the windshield.

"Look!" I cried, "look!"

"Who is it?" she asked, getting back into her seat.

"Popoki Nui—there he is!"

There he was, not a hundred feet ahead of us. He was a magnificent animal, carrying gracefully all the primitive splendor of his kind. He was fully seven feet long, his tail at least two and one-half feet.

"Oh!" It was all Giny could say. We both stared wide-eyed at the animal before us. Of course, we had no way of knowing that it was the one that haunted our lake. Yet, it could be, for they wander over wide reaches of territory.

The creature was not long in our sight. He crossed the road without looking in our direction and disappeared into the thick second growth.

I drove off the road to give our excitement a chance to cool down before we continued our journey.

"What a sight!" Giny gasped. "But why did he have to be here? Why couldn't he have met us at Panther Palace or some place like that?"

I shook my head and kept staring at the spot where the animal disappeared.

My shopping of that day could have landed me in an
asylum. I asked the owner of the photo shop for five
pounds of onions and wanted the grocery clerk to develop some films. I pulled into a gas station and asked
for ten gallons of panther.

Finally, after a bewildering day, we arrived home
just as darkness began. Bobette and her fawns were
gone.

XI

STRANGE BEDFELLOWS

THERE was trouble in Hawaii. Moke's next letter told it as plainly as though his scratches had actually formed the words. Great pressure had been exerted on the pencil as it scrubbed back and forth, and we could easily picture the bombastic youngster as he "wrote" the thoughts that were consuming him. Twice the pencil point had broken under his enthusiasm, leaving exaggerated periods right in the middle of wavy horizontal lines. We didn't need Liliana's letter to know that great things were happening in the Paradise of the Pacific, but it did help us in learning what they were.

"There have been more raids on our neighbor's chicken coop," wrote our Hawaiian friend, "and undoubtedly it is a mongoose that is doing it. There have been no more feathers on Kimo's nose, but he is under strong suspicion. Our neighbors are patient people, but they cannot stand for such raids. Even now they keep a loaded gun handy and we fear that when the fatal shot is fired Kimo will be the one who receives it. Moke comprehends the situation and he is frantic. His love for his pet mongoose and chicken is heart-touching, and the two seem just as fond of him."

"Couldn't they cage up the mongoose?" I broke into

Giny's reading. "I don't like confining animals, but it might be the lesser evil."

"They've tried that," Giny replied, glancing ahead in the letter. Then she broke out into a little laugh. "Poor Moke—wait until you hear this. 'We built a large, wire cage for Kimo. He wouldn't stand for it. When we put him in it he was so frantic with fear I believe he would have injured himself. Moke was about as wild as he was, and cried in Hawaiian and English at the same time. We liberated Kimo, convinced that any fate was better than this. Now Moke has taken it on himself to guard his pets day and night. He will hardly take time to eat. He watches them all day long and if Kimo as much as looks toward our neighbor's house, Moke gathers him up in his arms and tries to rock him to sleep.' "

"But he can't watch him through the night," I interposed. "That is the time of real danger."

"Think not?" Giny smiled. "Listen to this. . . ." And she read on.

"Now we are looking upon something nightly which must be new to the whole world," Liliana's letter continued. "When bedtime comes, Moke gathers up Kimo and Ewa in his arms and takes them both to bed with him. Strangely they want to go. Ewa clucks and tries to understand it all, but Kimo nestles down most contentedly. If you have never seen a chicken, a mongoose, and a little Hawaiian boy cuddled up together (and I

presume you never have), you have missed one of the cutest sights this world could offer."

"Now I ask you—" Giny ceased her reading and looked up—"isn't it worth a trip to Hawaii just to see that?"

"If we only get there in time!" I answered, drumming the table impatiently. I counted on my fingers even as Moke was doing daily. "Five months is a long time. Lots can happen to a chicken and a mongoose in five months."

"Oh, why can't Kimo love all chickens in a more spiritual way—as he does Ewa?" Giny indulged in some wishful thinking. "I'm sure he gets enough to eat without raiding that neighbor's chicken coop."

"Instinct, reversion to type—all that sort of thing," I said discouragingly.

Giny disagreed. "We get too hard and fast in our theories. The capacity to learn is stronger and more important than is generally believed. Kimo has learned to respect one chicken; why couldn't he develop the same attitude toward the others?"

I was silent, in fact quite convinced that there was much in what Giny was saying. I have seen a mouse the constant companion of a cat, and watched the cat purr happily whenever the mouse came near—not with any sense of "here comes dinner." I have known of a rabbit and a snake who were raised together and enjoyed a lasting friendship. At our island home I have seen porcupines, skunks, raccoons, and foxes feeding out of the same pan. Indeed, we have looked upon much evidence supporting the thought that at work among living things there are powerful forces other than brute instinct and ungoverned ferocity.

We had something to write Moke to take his mind off his own problems temporarily. Bing, the baby song sparrow, and Boom, the encroaching cowbird youngster, were out of the nest. They had to be. Boom was so huge he boiled over the edges, and Bing had hopped onto a convenient twig just to get out of the crowd. Boom soon joined him there, and a more comical pair I never saw. Both young birds were yelling loud and mercilessly at the parents for food. The poor mother and father worked themselves to the point of exhaustion. Every ounce of strength was needed for chasing insects and depositing them in those two mouths which seemed never to close or to cease begging.

Boom was larger than either of his foster parents, but he had the cute baby ways about him that play upon the hearts of avian daddies and mothers. He fluttered his wings in a display of juvenile helplessness and dependency that got him his full share of family provisions— and then some.

Our account to Moke of these events in the song-sparrow nursery played up the plight of Bing a little too much, I presume. Moke's reply was swift and practical. Out of his air-mail envelope we drew a folded piece of paper, bearing some of his scribbling on the outside. Above it Liliana had written simply, "For Bing, compliments of Moke." We looked inside and there in one big blotch was the remains of a Hawaiian insect!

Bing and Boom soon reached the traveling stage. They were trailing their parents from tree to tree, from bush to bush, begging, begging, begging. Still the frantic parents labored on.

"I wonder that there is an insect left on this island," Giny said. "And when will Boom start feeding himself? He is large enough to eat a frog now!"

We never got an answer to that question, but we did look upon something that has led us to making unanswered queries ever since. One day we trailed the birds as they worked their way toward our camp site. The male song sparrow was absent—possibly exhausted and resting somewhere in the trees—and the female was carrying all the burden of providing for this strange family.

Bing and Boom were very good fliers by this time, and kept close to the parent bird. They even pecked at some insect larvae in the bark of trees, though they were still largely dependent on the efforts of the mother. We saw them very clearly as all three flew out into the open space near our campground. Bing was closest to the mother bird. He seemed to be a better flier than Boom, who came along in shorter flights. Both youngsters were crying constantly and begging with fluttering wings in the usual way.

Then we witnessed a strange thing. We heard a different kind of cry and looked up to see a female cowbird perched low in a bush in the direction from which the little family had come. She was watching the feeding with interest. Her call was repeated several times.

Then our attention was drawn to the strange behavior of Boom. He had ceased his baby cries and fluttering, and he stood still on the ground. As the cowbird continued to call, he became much excited and looked her way. He flew a few feet in the direction taken by the song sparrows, then, as the cowbird cry came again, he turned about and flew toward its source. For just a moment he tarried on a low bush, looking toward the song sparrows and giving some plaintive notes which might have been "Thanks, Mom, for all you've done" (though I doubt it). Then the female cowbird flew away and *Boom after her*.

We never saw Boom again. That evening we were asking ourselves questions which we have asked others since—but with no informative answers. Was this the cowbird mother that had originally placed the egg in the song-sparrow nest? Had she been keeping track of Boom through the days he was a nestling? Do cowbirds usually reclaim their young? We do not know, and no one else seems to know.

We talked late into the night, trying to piece our observations together and reach sound conclusions. We walked down to the lake shore to take in some of the beauties of the night. A rich stillness cloaked the north country, and the heavens were ablaze with starry loveliness.

"How little man really knows of what goes on in the world of nature!" I commented. "It seems to me we are always reading just the first page of this book."

"Yet, it is a wonderful page," Giny added. "It keeps us reaching for the whole volume. If we were able to gather facts the way we do apples, it wouldn't be half so——"

Giny never finished her sentence. From out of the darkness came the sound of an explosion that seemed to rock the very island we stood on. From distant shores the startling report echoed to us again and again.

"A shot?" Giny asked, grasping my arm.

"Yes—from a shotgun. Likely it was a buckshot shell."

"It seemed to be near the Clearing," she said apprehensively.

"Yes, I think it was," I said, sickened at the thoughts that assailed me. "A hunter probably—a violator."

As we listened we heard a car start up. It was an old one, rattling and backfiring as it got under way. Then it went deeper into the night, and we judged it to be following the forest road. When it had almost disappeared, we heard the wail of a siren. This died down and then all was silent.

Our hearts were heavy with foreboding.

"Sam," Giny said hesitantly, "should we go . . . to the Clearing?"

"No, I believe not now," I replied, feeling I knew all too well what had happened. "What is done is done. We can be of no help. Morning light will be better than shades of night in which to read the story."

XII

THE GREATEST PREDATOR

THE SKIES were as gray as our thoughts the next morning, as though nature too were dreading what the day might reveal. The shot we had heard the night before seemed to hang in the heavy, still air. Cheerlessly we paddled to the north shore and made our way into the Clearing. Birds sang as beautifully as ever, but their songs were wasted on us. Fiddlesticks and Freckles were there. There was no play in them, and Fiddlesticks did not strut. Instead, they ran aimlessly about, their intermittent sprints seeming to be without purpose or destination.

"Bobette is not here," Giny said. I knew by the look in her eyes she feared something neither of us had voiced as yet.

I shook my head and we walked on. Fiddlesticks and Freckles followed us at a distance. Their ears worked constantly and their tails switched nervously.

We reached the road. "Here are the tracks made by the car," I said, indicating a record left by tires having a smooth, deeply worn tread. "And here is where it turned around." Obviously the car had moved back and forth to go in the reverse direction. The wheels had spun as effort was made to get under way quickly. There

117

were many tracks made by human feet in the sand. Leading out into the brush at one side was a strip where the grass and low bushes had been broken down as something heavy was dragged forth. I started in the direction this trail took.

"I'll wait here, if you don't mind," Giny said apprehensively.

"Do so," I agreed. "This may not be a pleasant sight."

It was extremely unpleasant, to put it mildly. There in the brush, fifty feet from the roadside, was the ghastly evidence that a deer had been killed and dragged away. The path showed it was a good-sized animal. This was not the work of a wolf or a panther. A greater predator had done this. The story was easy to piece together. Near the point where the car turned around lay an empty buckshot shell.

"The violators came down the road from the east," I explained to Giny. "There were two or more in the car, and they probably had a powerful flashlight. Then they saw the eyes of a deer reflecting their light. While one kept the light on the deer, the other one fired the shot. He couldn't miss with buckshot at that distance. The deer went down. The men dragged it out, put it in the car and drove away. It is an old story up in this country."

"Sam," Giny said earnestly, "was this . . . was this Bobette?" She held back the question as long as possible, dreading the answer.

I looked at Fiddlesticks and Freckles, who were close to us now, sniffing at the trail left through the brush when the violators dragged the dead deer away.

"I believe it was," I said, disliking my own voice. "It was a large animal they took. Bobette was large and this is her homeland. The two fawns are alone, and they are distressed. Everything indicates it was Bobette— we may as well face it."

Giny was silent.

"Bobette," I went on meditatively. "She had the cunning and wisdom necessary to protect her family from the normal hazards of the forest. She could outwit the coyotes and wolves and even a panther. But this strange creature man, who could slip up on her in the night, blind her with a strong light and strike her down from a long distance, was too much for her."

"And now?" Giny was at the point of tears. "Now, who will protect Fiddlesticks and Freckles? Doesn't a violator know that his shot may really claim three victims instead of just one? Doesn't such a person care?"

Bitterness could not help the situation, however, and we wasted no more words. Making such notes as I thought might be helpful, we went back to the island, and then to the headquarters of the game warden. Here we learned that the violator had been captured. The warden had trailed the car the night before and it was his siren that we had heard after the shot. The violator was convicted and fined heavily.

No doubt this punishment by law was necessary and might help prevent more violation of game laws. But it was small consolation for us. Whatever was done did not bring Bobette back.

Our concern now was for Fiddlesticks and Freckles. We returned to the Clearing in the afternoon and found them haunting the spot where their mother had last been seen. We knew that they were still at the nursing stage, and so we had brought with us two nippled bottles of milk. For two hours we tried to get near them, or to draw them close to us. They were obviously hungry, and kept nibbling at green things. Bobette had been training them to eat other things before the day of complete weaning came. But milk was still the main item on their menu.

"Oh, if I only knew just a few words in their language," Giny said desperately. "How do you tell them that this bottle holds something good for them? It seems as if our victory would come if only they would feed from our hands."

With great patience, and her deep love for living things, she followed the fawns about, talking with them, pleading with them. They moved away cautiously, keeping the distance that Bobette had taught them was proper in dealing with human beings. Once Freckles stood still until Giny got close enough to sprinkle a few drops of milk on her nose, but then she became frightened and ran away. Fiddlesticks too permitted one close approach, then dashed our hopes by snorting and racing off into the woods.

Evening was approaching, and we discovered that Fiddlesticks and Freckles were not the only hungry ones. So engrossed were we in this problem that we had not eaten all day long. Reluctantly we paddled back to the cabin.

Just before we got into the canoe, Giny called me to see something she had discovered in the sand. "Look, Sam," she said, pointing down. "As if we didn't have enough to worry about already!"

"The panther!" I exclaimed, looking down at huge tracks. "What a time for him to show up!"

"I don't believe these tracks were here this morning, or we would have seen them. Did he just come?"

"Perhaps," I said. "If only we could get Fiddlesticks and Freckles to the island."

"I have been thinking about that," said Giny. "But we can't get them even close enough to us to feed them. Did you ever feel more frustrated and helpless?"

"Never," I agreed. "Frustrated, helpless and starving. Let's get something to eat; maybe we can think more clearly then."

At the cabin we prepared some food, but it didn't taste right and we ate but little. Our minds were on those two speckled little orphans facing their first night in the great forest without Bobette's protection. We stood looking out our window at the deepening gloom. Loony Coon came to the door and Giny gave him the rest of our dinner.

"Sam," she said, in that tone that indicates the coming of an idea.

"Yes?"

"Would it be too foolish for us to take our sleeping bags and stay at the Clearing tonight? Maybe our presence there would offer some protection to the fawns. Wolves and Popoki Nui might not be so apt to come."

"I've been thinking of that," I replied, "but I hesitated to suggest it. We could pitch our tent and——"

"Let's do it!" she said anxiously. "I don't want them to go through this night alone."

Soon we were paddling toward the north shore, our tent and sleeping bags aboard. At the Clearing we found Fiddlesticks and Freckles still about, though with night coming on they were more timid of us than before. Selecting a favorable spot in the edge of the timber, we pitched our tent and spread our sleeping bags within it.

Fiddlesticks and Freckles became curious about the tent and came rather close. We had milk for them and took this occasion to offer it with all the pleading and persuasion we could muster, but they did not come to us. Instead, they walked away and disappeared into the forest. We kept watch over the area until late in the night when from sheer exhaustion we crawled into our sleeping bags and went to sleep.

The sun was shining when we awakened. The Clearing was vacant except for a snowshoe rabbit who went bounding away as we came out of our tent. We paddled back to the island for some breakfast. As we walked up the path from the pier, Giny grasped my arm and in a tone of delight said, "Sam, Sam, look!"

There, standing at the cabin door, looking at us as if saying, "Now where in the world have you been?" were Fiddlesticks and Freckles!

"Fine thing," I exclaimed. "While we stand guard all night over at the Clearing, facing panthers, wolves, bears and rhinocerpusses, you swim back and sleep on the island!"

"Surely—didn't Bobette teach them to do that?" On Giny's face was the first smile I had seen in nearly two days.

XIII

HUGGING AN OCTOPUS

THE ISLAND seemed filled with fawns that morning. It was all Fiddlesticks and Freckles, but they gave the impression that a dozen of their kind were haunting the woods about our cabin. Everywhere we looked, one or the other was peeking out at us. From behind our buildings, out of the balsam thicket, from back of our red pines and from among the birches, their little faces stared at us with inquisitive expressions.

"I know they are hungry for milk," Giny said. "What are we going to do?"

"They're nibbling at leaves," I observed.

"Yes, but they're not satisfied. You can tell that by the way they act. Bobette was still nursing them, and I believe they must need milk."

"Well, let's try a pan," I suggested. "To approach them with a bottle frightens them too much. The pan may be better."

Fiddlesticks and Freckles didn't think so. They finally approached the pan we set out for them, but just as Freckles was lowering her nose to it, Fiddlesticks pawed it with his foot, splashing milk in Freckles' face and sending the pan on a noisy journey across the ground. The two fawns left in a hurry, and thereafter gave the pan a wide berth, eying it suspiciously.

"It has to be the bottle," Giny affirmed. "Let's just keep after them. If once we can get them to taste the milk and know that it comes from the bottle, I'm sure they will feed that way."

Keep after them we did—all day long. Never have two animals been more flattered, cajoled and coddled.

"If Fiddlesticks believes what he is hearing, he is going to be more conceited than ever," Giny said as we made our twentieth approach to the animals. "Come, you beautiful, sweet things. You're just the loveliest things alive, yes, you are. . . ." She continued to shower endearing and complimentary words on them in siren tones.

Fiddlesticks and Freckles regarded all this as a sort of game. They watched our approach with interest, caution and perhaps a little amusement. Sometimes they would take several short steps in our direction, just to let us think we were winning. They eyed the bottle and ran their tongues out and in as if in anticipation. Tantalizingly they let us get nearly close enough to touch their noses, and then, just when we thought we were about to win—away they went! Time after time this was repeated, until Giny and I sank to a log discouraged.

While we sat there, Bing, the baby song sparrow, and his mother came along. Bing was getting all the attention now and literally ate it up. If the mother bird knew that Boom was gone, she did not slacken her efforts because of it. Bing was getting the insect harvest meant for two. He was flying very well now, but still teased his mother with fluttering wings and begging *cheeps*.

"She just pokes his food down his throat, doesn't she?" Giny noticed. "No mother pampering there. She doesn't coddle and coax him to eat his vitamins, and sprinkle sugar on everything so Junior will like it. She just rams the food in so far he has no choice in the matter."

"Maybe that is an idea we can adopt," I said, brightening with hope. "Perhaps I could grab Fiddlesticks and hold him while you actually put that nipple in his mouth. When he has his first swallow, I'll wager he will go on eating and thank us for what we have done."

Giny gave a gesture of hopelessness and nodded agreement. It wasn't long before I wished sincerely I had never thought up that idea.

Fiddlesticks and Freckles were on the west side of the island when we found them again. Here is a small hill that has a rather steep slope leading down to the lake. They looked up at us as we approached as much as to say, "You folks just love to play, don't you?"

We moved up on them slowly, step at a time, as we had done so many times previously. They watched the routine. It was old stuff to them now. Fiddlesticks bit off a blade of long grass, and chewed it down inch by inch as we approached. Giny reached forward with the nippled bottle of milk that we had been trying so desperately to sell them.

"Oh, Frecklesticks and Fiddles, you ceautiful breatures," Giny pleaded, her tongue tied in knots from constant use. "Here is some mice nilk."

"Just for two fovely lawns," I contributed. Then we both broke out in such boisterous laughter that Fiddlesticks and Freckles departed hurriedly for distant places. They completely circled the island, and finally returned to find us striving to suppress the kind of giggles that made tears flow down our cheeks. Now it was the fawns who stalked us, obviously much puzzled at this new mood. Their eyes protruded farther than usual, their ears pointed forward, and their noses reached toward us as they strove to understand.

"It's all right, pets," Giny said, with a few last little giggles thrown in. "We're just silly, that's all. Come now, take a taste of this." The bottle was held toward them once more.

Fiddlesticks was plainly interested. He stretched and stretched toward the much-offered food, until his nose was almost touching it. Giny tilted the bottle slightly and a drop fell on the fawn. He licked it off and apparently liked it. Another drop hung to the nipple, and he licked that one too.

Then I did something against my better judgment, against all I had learned from experience and against all sound reasoning. I lunged forward suddenly and snatched Fiddlesticks up in my arms, holding him by his mid-section.

It is a physical impossibility to grasp an armload of a cyclone, but I am sure after holding that fawn I know what the sensation would be. Another similar experience would be the hugging of an octopus. Fiddlesticks was all frantic wiggles, terrific twists and violent jumps. His legs struck and struggled so fast I thought he had a dozen of them. His tail went around like a spinning wheel and his head hit me three times with such force as to make me dizzy. In addition he was giving that little sheeplike bleat which a fawn can use but never does unless he figures things are pretty severe.

Somewhere in the midst of all this melee I could hear Giny's voice. "Now, little fellow, don't be afraid, here—have some nice milk." Fiddlesticks didn't want any nice milk. He just wanted his liberty, and there was nothing I would rather have given him. My problem was how to get rid of him. I couldn't just drop him, as I wanted to. I bent over, hoping that those flying hoofs of his would touch the ground and be calmed a bit. As I did, he gave a final lurch that surpassed all known lurches. He went to the ground all right, and so did I— head over heels down the hill right into the water!

It was rather deep at that point and I went completely out of sight. As I emerged, I was impressed with the silence. Through squinting eyes I could see that the fawns were gone. Giny was looking at me with an expression that indicated there were no words quite equal to the occasion. I walked dripping up to her, expecting a caustic comment, and dreading it. Finally she said simply, "You frightened my fawns."

"I frightened your fawns!" I burst forth. "Here I am practically drowned, and your only comment is that I frightened your fawns."

"If you had to go swimming," she said, ignoring my words, "why didn't you choose some other time and place? There are dry clothes up in the cabin. When you have changed, come out and apologize to Fiddlesticks and Freckles. No doubt we'll have to start all over again in gaining their confidence."

I trudged up toward the cabin, my shoes gushing and slushing all the way. It took a little while to transfer myself into dry clothes. Then I went out in the yard expecting the rest of the scolding I knew I deserved.

"Quiet, please," I heard Giny's voice coming from a point near the lake. "Don't disturb this, or you'll get thrown in the lake again."

There were Giny, Fiddlesticks and Freckles, all in a huddle. Freckles was enthusiastically nursing on the bottle that Giny held for her. The fawn was under a strain, her legs twitching as if she meant to run any moment, but she was eating Giny's offering, and liking it.

Fiddlesticks stood several feet to one side, watching

all this intently. Then moving with extreme caution, a step at a time, he edged up toward the bottle. He extended his nose as far as possible, and reached out with his tongue to lick the drops that were escaping from Freckles' chin.

"This is what did it," Giny explained, holding up the birdcall. "Am I grateful for that thing!"

XIV

FOREBODINGS

THE WESTERN sky glowed with crimson and the silent shades of evening were creeping through the forest. There was a feeling of triumph in our hearts. Fiddlesticks and Freckles had eaten of food offered them by our hands!

"Maybe it's a small incident in this big world," I remarked to Giny, "but it seems very important right now, doesn't it?"

"It *is* important," Giny insisted. "It is a victory, a triumph of love over fear—and that is mighty important. It proves something vital to life." She walked over to the window and looked out. Her face lighted with a smile, and she called me to her side. "Look, Sam," she exclaimed. "They're playing."

There, a short distance from our cabin, we could see the fawns, a little dim in the gathering gloom, playing just as we had seen them in the Clearing. They rose on their hind feet and boxed, they did their funny little dance, they staged races through the brush.

"Happy, aren't they?" Giny said warmly. "It is hard to believe that only forty-eight hours ago they lost their mother. How quickly they have recovered!"

"Wild things are that way, Giny. They do not brood

132

over yesterday and they do not dread tomorrow. They live in the present—today is enough of unfoldment for them. Look at them: their stomachs are full, they are free, they have each other for companionship. The forest is green with harvest for their future needs. They won't let any regrets or forebodings take away the joy of this moment. There is a lesson in this—particularly for me."

"Why do you say that? Aren't you happy in all this day has brought?"

"Oh, I have a nagging thought that hampers my pleasure."

"And pray tell, what is that?" Giny faced me. "Are you grieving for Bobette?"

"No," I replied. "That's over, and I won't permit myself to dwell on it."

"Is it the panther or the other predators?"

"No, we'll just have to help the fawns the best we can with that problem."

"Then what is it?"

"Well, it is that bow-and-arrow hunting season. There is to be one in September, and the hunters will be privileged to take one deer of any kind."

"Not a speckled fawn, surely."

"Yes, even a speckled fawn may be shot. Fiddlesticks and Freckles, if they wander out of our Sanctuary into hunting territory, will be legal game."

"You mean that anyone would call it sport to shoot

an arrow into such creatures as these?" Giny pointed out at the rollicking creatures, and looked increduously at me.

"Yes, and I wonder how much we are handicapping them," I continued. "In a way, we are breaking down Bobette's training. She taught them to be cautious of human beings. We are teaching them to be friendly to men. Bow-and-arrow hunters, being notoriously poor shots on the average, must get close to their victims. Are we preparing Fiddlesticks and Freckles for such a fate?" I considered the situation for a moment, then added, "We can't present them with a life of ease and safety, but I would like to help them reach their first winter. Bobette would have cared for them until near yarding time. Then they would be with a small herd of deer and gradually turn to independent lives. By spring they would be experienced and have at least an even chance to meet the challenges of forest life. It just seems to me the greatest danger they must pass through, the one that finds them least prepared, is that bow-and-arrow season."

We both reflected on the unpleasant thought. The fawns raced away through the brush, and we could hear them as they completely circled the island. Then Giny spoke spiritedly. "Listen here, young man," she said: "nothing is going to take my happiness away from me this moment. I am going to be like Fiddlesticks and

Freckles and accept all the joy of right now, and not let it be destroyed by anything that has happened or may happen. We are doing what is best for the present, aren't we?"

I nodded.

"They need milk and we have found a way to give it to them. We are making them feel at home on the island where there is greatest safety right now. So we are doing the best we can. When hunting season comes we will do the best we can then, too. This is the time for gratitude and happiness, and let's not refuse the blessings spread before us."

I smiled my agreement to her good logic, and we looked and laughed at the clown act the two fawns were putting on.

"We ought to do something to celebrate this wonderful day," Giny said enthusiastically. "We have had a victory, and people celebrate victories. We should have a feast, or a campfire party, where we could sing and make our joy known. This would be an evening to have our friends together."

"Good idea," I agreed. "We have done so little with our friends this summer."

"Too much Fiddlesticks and Freckles, I suppose," said Giny. "If we had a telephone I would try to assemble a group now."

"But we have no telephone, and neither do most of

our friends. But is there any reason we shouldn't do our own celebrating, even if we can't get others to join us? Let's have a campfire!"

"And invite Fiddlesticks and Freckles!"

"And have popcorn and songs—come on, what are we waiting for?"

It wasn't long until the trees about our campfire site were lighted with the glow of dancing flames. We put on some pine to make the fire burn high, some cedar to make it crackle and talk, and some oak to make coals glow long after the flames had died down. The night was still and we could hear the voice of the fire echo back to us.

Fiddlesticks and Freckles came up while we were laying the fire, but once it started to burn, they left for the far side of the island. This fire business was something new in their experience. Maybe Bobette had some way of telling them about such strange things. Wild things soon learn that the forest fire is the worst enemy of all. It not only threatens them directly, but destroys their forest homes and their food.

"All fires are bad fires to the animals," I remarked to Giny. "They do not know that a fire under control is a friendly thing. Maybe the fawns will learn."

We completely surrendered to the beauty and harmony of the night. The very atmosphere seemed to express Robert Browning's words: "God's in His heaven—All's right with the world!" Such moments in nature are precious, and they leave a lasting blessing in the heart. I strummed on my guitar, and we sang a few favorite songs.

"Listen!" Giny said suddenly. "I hear voices."

I had noticed the sound too, and we stepped beyond the fire to hear more clearly. What sound in human experience is sweeter than singing across still waters? The song we heard was a familiar one—the "Barcarole" from *The Tales of Hoffmann*. Soon we made out canoes, three of them, approaching our island over the glassy waters. The paddling was being done in rhythm to the song.

"It's Ada, Ray and June!" Giny said excitedly.

"Yes and others. Maybe they got our message or our mood. Maybe there are telephones we don't know of."

Soon the canoe bows grounded on the sands of our island, and our friends stepped ashore. Ada, Ray and June, our long-time friends and companions on many north-woods adventures, were there, with their usual smiles and good humor. The others of the party were neighbors from the shores of near-by lakes.

"We couldn't resist the call," Ada was saying. "The night was perfect for a campfire party, and it has been so long since we had one. We gathered everyone up and came over as a little surprise. And here you have the fire all ready for us. Aren't you nice?"

"But where is the popcorn?" asked Ray. "We want popcorn, don't we, folks?"

The whole party agreed. While Giny went to the cabin for the corn, the popper and dishes, our guests circled the campfire. Now there was new strength to our songs, and the evening rose to a higher level of merriment. We raked a few coals to one side so the corn could be popped there, and then added logs to send the flames high in the other portion of the fireplace.

Soon the popcorn was ready, though it was difficult to decide which was the more toasted, the cooks or the corn. A huge pan was heaped high with the white kernels and placed near the fire until the butter was melted to pour on it.

Conversation turned to Fiddlesticks and Freckles, whose story was known in part to our guests. Ray had heard of the killing of Bobette, and one object of this evening's trip was to learn if there were any way in which he could befriend the fawns. All were delighted to learn of Giny's triumph in feeding the creatures that day.

"And if your falling in the lake had anything to do with it, we hope it happens daily," Ray said.

"Could we see them?" June asked anxiously. "Would it be possible to approach them if we went across the island?"

"I wonder if I could call them up," Giny said. "This is all so new to us we don't know what to expect as yet. Let me try."

She produced the birdcall from her pocket, and began twisting some squeaks from it. "This is what brought them to me today," she said, noting that everyone was watching her skeptically. "Maybe they'll get the idea that it means some sort of a reward if they obey it."

"Maybe they won't too," Ray put in. "That doesn't sound like anything that would interest a fawn. You might expect a mouse to come, or a bird, but why in the world would a deer listen to that?"

Giny kept on playing weird melodies on the contrivance and then, discouraged with the lack of results, put it down. "Well, it worked before," she said. "Perhaps they have to be real hungry to hear it. I'm not getting any response now."

"I don't know," said Ada. "It seems to me you're getting a pretty good response. Look over there."

She pointed toward a small cluster of hemlock saplings. There, barely within range of the campfire light, stood the two fawns. They were all attention, searching about the group for some explanation of this gathering, and for the whereabouts of the fascinating squeaks. A little breathy "O-o-o-o-o-h" swept over the group, and Giny ground out some birdcalls.

Even as we watched, the fawns discovered the pan of popcorn sitting on the ground. One of them walked toward it with high and fancy steps, his head held up in royal dignity. A pan of food sitting on the ground? He had seen such a thing before. Stretching his nose to it, he became excited at the delightful aroma he encountered. Carried away with enthusiasm, he struck forward with one foot, striking the pan and sending a small blizzard of popcorn all over the ground. Then the two fawns proceeded to feast on the kernels.

"Good friends, we want you to meet Fiddlesticks and Freckles," Giny said above the laughter. "And that *was* your popcorn."

XV

CHIMP, CHAMP AND CONFUSION

FIDDLESTICKS and Freckles were still on the island the next morning. A few squeaks on the birdcall brought them to our door—with appetites equal to a quart of milk each. We were more solicitous than an English innkeeper with royal guests.

"Were your beds comfortable, your highnesses?" I said, bowing low to them, as Giny served their breakfasts. "Did our woodpecker alarm clock call you too early? Would you like the sun to come a bit later tomorrow? May I polish your hoofs?"

The two fawns kept sucking on the nippled bottles Giny held, making plenty of noise about it too. "He's silly, pets," Giny said. "What he is trying to say is that we want you to live on the island where you're safe. It is just a little island, I know, but it is cozy and we'll bring you lots of food. You can spill a pan of popcorn every day if you want to. I'll do a washing for you to drag in the dirt and plant more flowers for you to eat or step on. How about it babies, will you stay?"

But Fiddlesticks and Freckles just ate all the louder and refused to commit themselves.

Another day and the two deer began to get acquainted with the animals about the island. They came upon the

141

woodchuck hole, and nearly turned a back flip when Patty stuck her head out suddenly. They recovered quickly, however, and stared at the small creature. Fiddlesticks struck one of his hypnotic poses, as fixed as a statue as he studied the homely little face that returned his glare. He met his match that day. No one can outstare a woodchuck. Fiddlesticks tried his best. He

looked and looked and looked but Patty looked right back at him. After five minutes of this silent contest, Fiddlesticks conceded victory. Switching his tail at some pestersome flies, he trotted into the bushes, while Patty continued to stare at the place he had been.

The meeting with our two chipmunks included a moment of high excitement. It happened when the fawns were having their evening meal, compliments and courtesy of Giny. The chipmunks were working hard at storing the peanuts which I dealt forth in quantity. One chipmunk we knew as Chimp, the other was Champ. Champ was the world's champion peanut carry-awayer. It is common for a chipmunk to take three large peanuts in his cheeks at one time—but Champ regularly carried five! Hence Chimp, to get as many peanuts as Champ, had to make nearly twice the number of trips. There was fierce competition between them, resulting in many a scuffle and chase.

No place was sacred or taboo to Chimp and Champ in their tireless pursuit of peanuts. They took them from my pockets, they ran about inside my shirt seeking them, they gathered them in my hair, they took them from my lips. With their cheeks bulging like balloons, they would race away to store their treasures in their underground homes, and then frantically dash back to get some more. I believe they would carry away a bushel if they had the opportunity.

Right when their excitement had reached a high pitch and they were both bounding back to me, I tossed a peanut in the direction of the fawns. It lodged on Fiddlestick's back. Without hesitation Chimp jumped high and landed on the astonished deer. Champ wasn't to be outdone, and he made a mighty leap and joined Chimp. Fiddlesticks, outraged at anything taking such

liberty with his royal back, rared up, jerking the nipple off the bottle. Milk spurted and Fiddlesticks bolted. The chipmunks leaped desperately out into space, and landed on Freckles. She whirled about, jerking the nipple off her bottle, and more milk splashed to the ground and on Giny. The chipmunks made another leap and, landing on the ground, got in a rough-and-tumble fight, each blaming the other for everything that had happened. It all took place in much less time than it takes to tell it.

"You caused all that—I could annihilate you!" Giny exclaimed, brushing milk from her clothes. "Why did you toss that peanut on Fiddlesticks?"

There was no answer to her question, so I simply said,

"Let's get some more peanuts—and some more milk."
We did.

The meeting of our fawns and raccoons the evening
of this busy day was scarcely less exciting than that with
the chipmunks. The raccoons came in great numbers
that night. At one time we counted twenty-two of them
on our front steps. It was at that moment that Fiddlesticks and Freckles came dashing out of the brush. Perhaps something had frightened them on the far side of
the island, or maybe it was only a routine run, but it was
enough to put a sudden end to the raccoon party. When
the two fawns swished past our front door, those raccoons literally flew apart. Two of them tried to get into
the woodchuck's hole at the same time, and didn't fit.
Some of them went scratching up trees. Others went
into the bushes as if jet-propelled.

Fiddlesticks and Freckles came to an abrupt stop,
then walked toward the several pans of dog food we had
given the raccoons. Coon faces looked out at them from
behind balsam trees and alder bushes, from up in
birches and pines. Fiddlesticks walked up to each food
pan, sniffed at it, and with obvious disapproval kicked
it over, spilling the contents on the ground. Then he
strutted into the night, followed by Freckles. The raccoons returned, uncomplainingly cleaned up the mess—
and ate it.

Days passed, and our two fawns stayed on. Was it
because of the food? Or had these young creatures

some knowledge that the island was a refuge for them? We could not know, but we were grateful for whatever held them there.

We wrote the sad news about Bobette to Liliana, asking her to convey it to Moke if she approved of doing so. Her reply, and his, came by return mail. "I told Moke about Bobette," her letter ran. "I try to protect his thoughts from the errors of the world as much as possible. However, we do not misrepresent things. Moke is of sturdy stuff. He is equal to what life demands of him. He was sorry about Bobette, but now his great concern is Fiddlesticks and Freckles. He wants you to put a leash on them and lead them around. That is something I would like to see. If you attempt it, I hope you have better success than he has. A friend made a little harness for Kimo. You never saw a more obstinate mongoose. When that harness is on him, he won't do one thing other than curl up on the floor. Apparently he thinks he is being punished. For hours after he has had it on, he cowers and hides. I guess the harness is out. You can have it for your fawns, and I have no doubt they will like it—just the way Kimo does.

"One month is just about gone now, so it is only four until you come. Moke says the month passed is the one he counted on his thumb. He keeps his thumb folded in his hand, and every day counts the other four fingers. You must feel his little heart tugging on yours all the time."

There was a postscript which said, "Our neighbor has lost two more chickens."

The fawns came for dinner early that evening. They no longer waited for the birdcall to summon them, but walked boldly up to the cabin door, demanding service. We didn't respond as quickly as they thought we should this particular time, so Fiddlesticks pawed at the door and cut a long gash in the screen—a great convenience for mosquitoes.

After giving the two deer their dinner and setting some food out for the raccoons, Giny and I went for a canoe ride. The canoe had been neglected since the coming of Fiddlesticks and Freckles to the island, as our time was entirely consumed with the fawns. Now the call of smooth waters and distant shores was irresistible, and we launched out onto the lake.

The noises of bullfrogs dominated the night. The season in which these noisy creatures call was at its height. As we neared a swampy area their voices were so strong Giny and I could not converse in ordinary tones. Tree toads added to the volume.

"If one didn't know what that sound was, wouldn't it startle him?" asked Giny. "Why, it might well come from an animal the size of a cow."

"Even a whoopingdinger?" I asked.

"Yes, even a whoopingdinger. I wonder if we will ever hear Popoki Nui again. Do you suppose it would sound as weird and frightening as it did that first time?"

There was no need for me to answer. A few moments later, from out of the darkness in the direction of the Clearing, came the cry itself. The echoes, nearly as fierce as the original, rebounded to us from distant shores. The cry was repeated a second and a third time. Perhaps we were hearing the voices of two panthers.

"What did you discover—did it affect you as before?" I asked, when I could get my breath.

"Just as much," Giny said, with a deep breath. "I could *never* get used to it. And you?"

"My hair stood on end," I confessed. "In fact, both of them did. Let's go back to the island and tell Fiddlesticks and Freckles how lucky they are."

The fawns were not there to receive the message. They had left the island.

XVI

HARTS AND FLOWERS

WE HOPED Fiddlesticks and Freckles would return to the island for their morning meal, but they did not. Working the birdcall constantly, we wandered the trails about Vanishing Lake. An old blue jay came up to see what bird was doing all this squeaking, but decided we didn't look much like his kind and flew away, scolding at the top of his voice. There was no response from our fawns.

Next we went to the Clearing and squeaked out a symphony all over the place, but our pets were not there. We found what might have been their tracks in the sands of the road, but of course there were many fawns in the big forest who could make such prints. The alarming thing was that Popoki Nui had left his autograph in the road too.

"Do you suppose he got them?" Giny worried.

"Now, now," I said, striving to voice an assurance I didn't entirely feel. "Let's think with our hopes and not our fears. Anyway, the big cat does not entirely consume the game he catches. If he had made a kill here, we would find evidence of it."

"Negative assurance," Giny grumbled, far from satisfied. "Why didn't we bring our sleeping bags here and stay last night?"

10—F.A.F.

"I thought of suggesting it," I replied. "But we had no idea where they had gone. They may have gone into the Vanishing Lake area, or even a section of the forest in which we have never seen them."

"All right—I'll work to keep my faith high," Giny said, "but it isn't easy. Suppose we separate so we can cover a larger territory. I'll circle the big hill to the north and you work to the south."

"And we'll meet here in an hour?"

"Right."

When we came back, Giny had nothing to report but the seeing of a big snowshoe rabbit. My comment was that "I didn't see a living thing." These were carefully chosen words. I was holding back a secret from Giny, rather a gruesome one. Far back in the woods, near the edge of a wide swamp, I had come upon the unhappy evidence of a panther kill. The victim was a speckled fawn. However, there was no way of knowing what fawn this might be, and so I saw no reason to torture Giny's thought by telling her of my find.

"I still have confidence that they will return when they get hungry," I said, as we made our way to our canoe on the beach. "I remember Bobette when she was a fawn—and what a problem she was. Once when she was very tiny and had just come to the Sanctuary, she disappeared and was gone all day. There were a number of people at the Sanctuary, and we searched all day long for her. Finally we found her, not fifty feet from the cabin, perfectly concealed under some small balsam trees. We had passed her a dozen times, but failed to see her. We may have passed Fiddlesticks and Freckles in our search. At this age they look just like the ground flecked with spots of sunlight."

Giny didn't answer. We paddled back to the island to give rather halfhearted attention to accumulating desk work.

As evening approached, two bottles of milk were prepared and left standing hopefully in warm water. They were never used. We watched the waters for creatures coming our way, and vainly listened for the splash that attends the swimming of deer. A few raccoons made their way to the island slowly and soundlessly, but that was all.

Early the next morning we went searching again, carrying bottles of milk with us. Neither the Clearing nor Vanishing Lake offered any news of our pets. Rather aimlessly we cruised the shore line in our canoe. We paddled our way through the thoroughfare that leads to the next lake on our chain. Here we came upon a long-time friend and neighbor doing some early-morning fishing from his pier.

"Wish you had been here with your camera last evening," he called, after greetings had been exchanged.

"Why, was there something special?" I asked.

"Yes, you sure would have got some good pictures. We were attacked by wild beasts!"

"You were? Tell me about it."

"Well—we were cooking dinner when I looked out the window, and there stood two fierce animals that would make your blood run cold."

"What in the world did you see?" I asked, wondering if panthers had ventured so close to a dwelling.

"Well—" our neighbor tempered his voice—"it was two of the cutest fawns you ever saw."

Giny whirled about so suddenly she nearly upset the canoe. "Two fawns—tell us about them. Were they friendly? Did they come to you?" She talked so fast each word stepped on the heels of the one before it.

"Sort of friendly," said our friend, his eyes sparkling at the recollection. "When we started out the door they acted as if they would run away, so we stayed inside and watched them. One was so full of spots they were overlapping. And the other one—" he broke out laughing—"the other one had such a silly walk!"

"Did he hold his head high and curl his legs as he walked along—sort of like a circus horse," I asked excitedly, guiding the canoe toward the pier.

"Yep, that describes it," our friend agreed. "Like a circus horse. And do you know what that one did?"

He scowled in mock anger—casting a plug far out in the lake.

"What?" Giny and I said in unison.

"He came strutting right up to our flower boxes—and ate every last blossom there! Went the whole length of it, bit every one off, and chewed it down."

"Oh, that's a shame," Giny sympathized.

"Naw!" Our friend laughed. "We could have stopped him. We just stood there and watched him do it. Been a long time since I saw a fawn so close. Why, he was right outside the living-room window and we were just inside. They stayed about a half hour and then disappeared. It was the best evening we've had all summer."

"Tell you what I'll do," I said. "I'll buy you new flowers for your box. You get just what you want in town and tell me what they cost."

"Now why should you do that?" he asked.

"Because we're sure those are our fawns," Giny joined in. "They've been missing for two days, and we've been searching for them. It's worth all the new flowers you need to know they're safe."

"No, you don't buy me any flowers. I'll buy 'em myself," he said positively, making another cast and reeling in. "I want to get 'em planted so those little fellers will have something to eat if they come back. What do you call them?"

"Fiddlesticks and Freckles."

"Good names! Fiddlesticks is the one that struts?"

"He is."

Our friend sent a peel of laughter echoing about the lake, and then busied himself untangling a backlash in his fishline.

We hurried back to the island to get some milk ready. At four o'clock in the afternoon our customers came. Their presence was announced in no uncertain way. Giny was reading and I was at my typewriter. Suddenly we heard a sound at the back door, a ripping sound as though something were being torn to pieces. That is exactly what was happening. Fiddlesticks and Freckles both pawed at the screen door, making two long gashes in it with their sharp hoofs.

I never saw anyone move faster than Giny did. She grasped the two waiting bottles of milk and dashed out the screen door, not even pausing to note the damage. And I never saw hungrier animals than the two fawns that stood there looking at us. They acted as if they intended to swallow bottle and all. While they drank even more noisily than usual, she plied them with unanswered questions. Where had they been? Why did they go away? Did they see the panther? Would they stay on the island?

"I can tell you now that I found the remains of a fawn near the Clearing—the kill of a panther," I said.

"And now I can tell you that I found one too—on the side of the hill," she replied.

This adventure with our fawns was prophetic of many similar ones to come. Without any consideration of our worries and concerns, the creatures came and went repeatedly. It seemed to us that they chose exactly the wrong times to leave the island—just before a storm, when wolves were howling, the very night the panther was present. But they survived one journey to the mainland after another, and we were commencing to feel that they were able to take care of themselves. Bobette's training was serving them well. We noted evidence that they were gaining in strength: their runs were faster and their swimming was more powerful.

Realizing what type of problem we were facing, we tied ribbons about their necks. I proposed just red ribbons for the purpose, but Giny decided they should be red, white and blue. "Let's appeal to the patriotism of the folks that find them," she said. "It is a patriotic matter, for deer are important to America."

Fiddlesticks seemed to strut more than ever when decorated with that red, white and blue ribbon. It was made of knit material so it would stretch and come off if caught on the brush. With this means of identification, we began to learn how far these two young creatures were wandering. We had always thought of them being near the Clearing or Vanishing Lake. Now we heard of them five, ten, twelve and fifteen miles away. A surveyor saw them ten miles from our island, when he was running a line. A timber cruiser saw them at least twelve miles distant. They came up to a house five miles from us.

Other reports came in too. One distant neighbor had laboriously done a large washing and hung it out. She saw two fawns come into her yard, one strutting along, the other following meekly. Even as she watched, the strutter approached her washing, which was flapping in the breeze. The creature headed for the waving sheets, rared up on his hind legs, striking at them, connected with the clothesline, breaking it—and down went the washing into the dirt! This was before the advent of the red, white, and blue ribbons, but when we heard of it we had no doubt who the fawns were.

Fiddlesticks and Freckles became increasingly friendly; they took it for granted that everyone loved and wanted them, and they took advantage of the fact too. They developed a special aptitude for appearing at picnics. At a camp site on a lake ten miles to the north of us, some picnickers had just spread their table, when it was decided that everyone would take a quick swim before lunch. When they returned, there stood two fawns with ribbons on, calmly eating the combination salad that had been most carefully prepared. The bathers stood back until the fawns had finished. At another picnic, two young deer drank up all the fruit punch, and then tipped a picnic basket over, looking for more. At still another, where a tiny baby was being fed by a bottle, a fawn came out of the woods and timidly approached to within a few feet, eying the milk covetously.

Down the lake shore several miles from our cabin, a man was painting his summer cottage a copper red. Two fawns came out of the woods, and grazed about near the foot of the ladder on which the painter was working. He whistled at them and they just looked up at him but did not run. Then the two creatures drifted over to a small flower garden where with much difficulty this man had raised a few blossoms in spite of poor soil. "Yahoo!" the painter shouted. "Get out of that. Eat all the grass you want but let those flowers alone." The two fawns kept right on nibbling blossoms. Down came the painter, full of fight, waving a wet paintbrush menacingly. Yelling loudly, he rushed at the fawns. One of the animals ran away but the other just lifted his head and looked calmly at the excited man. "*'Raus mit* you! Vamoose! Scat!" he yelled, but the fawn didn't do any of them. Instead, he reached down and bit off one more flower. Disgusted and desperate, the man brought his paintbrush down on the rump of the fawn with a resounding *smack*. Away went the fawn, and the house painter did not see him again. We did. That night Fiddlesticks and Freckles were back on the island—Fiddlesticks with a large blotch of copper-red paint on his rump.

So it was that we worked and worried our way, and the fawns' way, through the summer.

"Well, kids," Giny said one evening as she fed the two orphans, "you may be a headache, but you're never a bore." That day we had retrieved them from the very center of town and brought them back to our lake in the rear seat of our car. They paid for their transportation by kicking several holes in the upholstery. That day, too, I had replaced the screen on our door for the sixth time.

"We're going to get you through to yarding time even if it puts us in the poorhouse," I said, scratching Fiddlesticks behind the ears. He was drinking with his usual vigor, and so was Freckles. "When are you giving up that bottle, old top?" I continued. "You're getting to be a big boy now."

"Oh, I hope they keep at it a little while longer," said Giny. "This brings them to the island. Let them be babies as long as they will."

"Yes, they'll wean themselves at the right time. We'll feed them as long as they accept it. It's been kind of a tough summer, hasn't it, Freckles?" I said, turning my attention to the other fawn. "But you got through July, and you got through August, and here comes September."

"Sam," said Giny soberly.

"Yes?"

"When does that bow-and-arrow season begin?" She asked the question reluctantly.

"September fifteenth."

"How long does it last?"

"Thirty days."

Giny drew in a deep breath, but said nothing.

XVII

ARCHERS AND ANXIETY

THE MORNING the bow-and-arrow hunting season opened, a pale haze hung on the north country. Distant horizons wore a thin, blue veil, and the sun rose as a great red ball so reduced in strength that we could look directly at it. The brilliant blush of autumn rested upon deciduous trees—maples in scarlet, oaks in maroon, aspens in orange and birches in yellow.

"What a spectacle!" Giny exclaimed as we looked out over our lake to the far shores. "It's a carnival, a Mardi Gras."

"A coronation, a royal feast," I added. "It never grows old, does it, this autumn spectacle?"

"Never! There is such *happiness* in it all." Giny's expression changed. "If only . . ."

"I know what you're thinking," I said, following her gaze into the distance. "If only we didn't know that out in that forest there is a small army of men wearing red jackets and red caps, with quivers of arrows slung on their backs and strong bows in their hands."

"And it is legal for them to shoot any deer—even a fawn." Giny shook her head in disapproval.

Fiddlesticks and Freckles were resting contentedly on the island that morning of peril. Even though they

were deer, they were in the doghouse, so to speak. To their insatiable appetites for garden flowers had been added another taste, even more deplorable. Some five miles away stood a small farm with a carefully tended and quite important vegetable garden. Here was a fine patch of tomatoes, which the farmer had nursed through early frosts and other hazards. The vines were laden with luscious red fruit. Fiddlesticks and Freckles, decorated with those identifying red, white and blue ribbons, had spent several hours in this patch, during which they sampled fully half of the tomatoes. It wouldn't have been so bad if they had taken a tomato or two and eaten them. But they took just a bite out of each, leaving the rest hanging on the vines to rot. The damage was done when the farmer discovered them.

He was admirably mild-tempered. He got the aggravating creatures in his car and brought them out to our landing. We wouldn't have blamed him if he had deposited them in the town dump. I paid for a lot of tomatoes we couldn't eat. He didn't want to take the money, but we thought it only fair that he should.

"A wild deer might do the same thing," he said.

"Yes, perhaps," I agreed. "But we made these fellows become unafraid of human beings, and that helps them do such stunts."

"Better watch 'em close," the farmer warned as he was leaving. "These bow-and-arrow fellers are comin'! Some of 'em like nothin' better'n a friendly animal like these—somethin' they can get close enough to. Be a shame to lose these critters." He patted the willing Freckles.

I went to town for supplies and found the villagers much disturbed about the archery season. Cars had been passing through with newly killed deer roped to the fenders. On a corner stood Old Timer, a guide well known throughout the north.

"The season's on," I said, greeting him. "Are you going out looking like Dan Cupid with a bow in your hand and arrows on your back?"

"Not me, son," he snapped. "I never saw nothin' like it. Been a hunter for sixty years, but I never killed a fawn. Here—look what's comin'."

A car went by with a very young speckled fawn on the fender.

"Hev I lived to see the day?" grumbled Old Timer, tightening his lips over his teeth. "An' they call that sport!"

As was my custom, I took to patrolling our game Sanctuary. I went to the Clearing. Just beyond the road, outside the protected area, were hunters. I could hear them laughing and calling to each other. One party of three men strayed across the road and into the refuge. I approached them and found them to be quite good sports. Plainly they had made a mistake and had no notion of violating the law. Good sportsmanship truly is a high virtue. If hunting must be done, let it be with respect for law and property rights and as humanely as possible. These men *were* good sports. They weren't just after game. The whole hunting trip was an excuse to be outdoors. They respected the quarry. Early that morning they saw a deer, they told me, but it was so far away they feared they might only wound it so they withheld their arrows. One member of the party had not even strung his bow. He carried a small camera and was getting his joy out of recording the autumn color.

The next group of hunters I found within the refuge provided a sharp contrast to the good sportsmen. Their coming into the closed area was no accident, though they pretended it was. Their insincerity was obvious. Their language was rough, their manner insolent.

"What do y'think—yu own th' whole earth?" one of them replied when I first told them they were on my property.

"No—I own only a small piece of it, a very small piece," I answered.

"An' yu won't let a guy come on it an' get a deer!" he said, endeavoring to make me the offender.

"No, the animals in this region have been protected until they are rather friendly. It wouldn't be fair to let hunters at them."

By the little cynical laugh that followed I saw that they had heard of this place and were there because the animals might be approachable. They were reluctant to leave, until I reminded them that I had taken their hunters' license numbers from the tags the law requires them to pin on their jackets. Through these the warden could easily find them. They went away murmuring, and I knew they intended to come back into the refuge unless I kept a sharp watch.

These experiences were often repeated as the season went on. The conservation warden devoted a portion of his time to watching for violation of our refuge, but his territory was vast and he could not be long in any one place. Our protection depended mostly on our own vigilance.

Fiddlesticks and Freckles made no special effort to

relieve our concern about them during these uncertain days. They came and went in their established routine. They would be on the island for two or three days, then gone for a day or two. During their journeys they wandered far beyond the protective borders of the refuge. Once a man who knew them saw them twenty miles to the north. Every foot of the territory through which they traveled in going to and returning from that distant point was in hunting regions. But they returned safely—and ripped the screen off the door for the eighth time to announce their presence!

We neared the end of the season. "Five more days." Giny sighed. "If we can just get through this last stretch, we can feel comparatively safe."

"Strange how we have forgotten the panther, isn't it?" I remarked. "Haven't heard him or seen his tracks during all this period."

"That's right, I had forgotten him," she agreed. "The hunters are so much greater a threat. Let's patrol the Sanctuary from dawn to dark every day until the season is closed!"

Patrol it we did. There were no more violators, though, and the number of hunters in the woods was greatly reduced. Most of them had calculated to come early, for as the animals are frightened by one attack after another they become more wary and difficult to find.

The last day was at hand. Giny and I were feeling

triumphant. Fiddlesticks and Freckles had left the island a day before, but they had done this so often we felt confident they could take care of themselves.

"I think I'll patrol the Clearing once more," I said.

"This time I'm going along," Giny declared. "This will be a sort of celebration. How wonderful that this hunting business is over!"

"Almost over," I corrected. "The season is on until sundown."

"Well . . ." She didn't say more, but got her jacket and we paddled to the north shore.

Some trees had discarded their leaves. Under a small hard maple we found the ground covered with leaves, making a carpet of brilliant red. The ferns had lost their summer green and the hillsides were coated with their golden autumn hues. Autumn flowers were everywhere. The air bore the fragrance of mingled pine needles, asters, dried ferns. We sang several campfire songs as we walked along.

In the distance now we heard a car coming down our forest road. We made our way toward a spot where it must pass. When it came in view we saw that it was a station wagon. The fenders bore evidence that the party had had a "successful" hunting trip. The bodies of two speckled fawns were roped on in the traditional way. The car came to a stop.

"Do you mind if I turn back?" Giny said, half-sickened at the sight. "I guess I can't stand such things."

"Please do so," I said. "I'll talk with them."

"Are you Sam Campbell?" a heavy voice called from the car.

"Yes, I am."

"Want to see you," the same voice said. The door opened and a man of huge frame got out, decked in hunter's costume. He walked toward me and I toward him. I could see that there were others in the car.

"We got your fawns," the man said as he approached. His voice had a tone of triumph and savored of joy.

"Oh," I managed to reply, my heart sinking. Then I added with effort, "Are you sure they were mine?"

"Oh, yes," he affirmed. "Sure they're yours—red, white and blue ribbons on. We've been watching for them ever since we came." He gave a delighted laugh.

I was struggling with temper and resentment. How could this stranger be so joyous over something he knew would hurt me deeply? I had no legal claim to the fawns. He was within his rights, but his attitude was hard to understand.

"Where did you find them?" I asked. We were close together now and I found him to be a pleasant-looking fellow.

"Ten miles north, near Butternut Lake." He laughed. "Had plenty of trouble getting them, but when we ate lunch they came right up to us and it was easy." Again came that laugh. It was incredible. With a sick feeling I looked toward the pitiful creatures on the distant car.

"Well, I hope you killed them outright," I said, yearning for one bit of comfort.

"Huh?" he said, looking at me in surprise.

"I just hope they didn't suffer."

"Suffer?" He looked at me puzzled. Then his eyes lighted, and he laughed. "Oh, I get it. You think those are your fawns on the fenders? Naw. I got 'em alive in back of my car. Where do you want them? I gotta get 'em out of there. They scratched up all the inside of the wagon and broke one window already. You never saw such lively things! I'd rather haul around a couple of bears. What'll I do with them?"

For the first time in my life I wanted to kiss a man. I tried my best to be calm, but it wasn't easy. "Turn them out right here," I managed to say. "This is all right. Just let them loose."

"Hey, fellows," he called to his companions. "Open up the back door. Let them sticks of dynamite out right here."

The door was opened, and out came Fiddlesticks and Freckles. They went racing around the Clearing in a great circle, the way they used to do when Bobette was with them.

"Look at 'em go!" the man shouted, along with his boisterous laugh. His companions joined him in his merriment. "And let me tell you something," he said emphatically. "We're cured—all of us. Them little things comin' right up and eatin' lunch with us! I'm never killin' another. If we had any way to bring them two others there back to life, we'd do it. We feel ashamed to take 'em home."

I don't know that I thanked the man, except with my heart. I was so confused I didn't get his name. We shook hands at least six times and then he drove away.

Giny and I stayed in the Clearing with Fiddlesticks and Freckles until the sun entered the mist on the western horizon. Once more it was just a huge red ball, so veiled that we could look right at it. Near the horizon it flattened out in appearance to egg shape, then inched its way down below the horizon. The instant it disappeared we gave a cry of triumph. The bow-and-arrow season was over!

Fiddlesticks went strutting across the Clearing, closely followed by Freckles. They disappeared into the darkening forest.

XVIII

TRIGGER HAPPY

NOVEMBER—*Moon of Barren Boughs!* There is a fascinating rugged grandeur to the forest in this month, sandwiched in between autumn and winter. The trees shed their colorful costumes and stand in powerful, primitive beauty, like athletes joyously facing challenging contests.

Leaves plucked by the wind whirl about and search out a place on the ground. Woven together in countless numbers, they form a blanket, covering up seedlings and ground plants, protecting them against the coming cold of winter. The forest and all its creatures are getting ready for winter, and for another spring.

November has always had a particular appeal to Giny and me. We love to hike forest trails to the musical *swish* of crisp, dry leaves under our feet. The tangled mass of leafless limbs overhead has a gripping orderliness, even though no two twigs point in the same direction.

Our animals were preparing for the frigid months ahead. Loony Coon and his tribe were dressed in thick, beautiful gray-black fur that made them look twice their normal size. Fiddlesticks and Freckles lost their spots and at the same time weaned themselves from bottle feeding. They dressed in a dark gray, which is what fashionable fawns wear at that season. Bing probably couldn't afford all new feathers, so his family took him south for the winter. Perhaps for the same reason Patty Sausage and her tribe curled up in their underground homes to sleep through until spring. This sleeping a winter away is right popular among forest children of the north—and bears, woodchucks, chipmunks, skunks, jumping mice, frogs, toads, turtles and many others indulge it to varying degrees.

"It's snowing, Sam!" Giny exclaimed as she looked out the cabin window. There was delight in her voice.

"Good—more power to it," I said, coming to her side.

Wildly racing gray clouds were sweeping by at low altitude, giving squalls of mixed rain and snow. Soon the windward side of trees were plastered white, though the warm earth melted each flake that touched the ground.

"Oh, for a real snow—a real, heavy, drifting snow!" There was a touch of prayer in Giny's words.

"You mean before the rifle-hunting season comes?" I asked.

"Yes. It would help the deer, wouldn't it?"

"Yes, it would." I looked up at the clouds but they gave us no encouragement. This was not the dull gray overcast that promises the heavy snowfall. Occasionally a space would appear between the massive, floating cloud mountains, whose vapors curled and twisted with the high wind. This was not a blizzard. It was merely the sowing of the seeds of winter.

"You've said that this rifle season will not be as great a threat to Fiddlesticks and Freckles as the bow and arrow?" she asked, meditatively.

"The law permits a hunter one buck with fork horns. Our fawns face no threat from the careful, law-abiding sportsmen."

"Only from the violator?"

"And the careless one who shoots first and looks later."

"How long is the season?"

"The last ten days of the month."

Giny was thoughtful. "There isn't much we can do, is there? Since the fawns stopped their bottle feeding they don't return to the island as frequently as they did."

"Well, let's put new, bright ribbons on them," I suggested. "Then have faith that every man is a good sport at heart."

Two days before the season began, our lake froze over with a thin coating of ice. Fiddlesticks and Freckles were on the island at the time. Then would follow a few days when the ice would be too thin to walk on, and too thick for swimming. They had to be content to stay home—and so did we. This period comes each year to the north country. We keep a supply of food on hand to prepare for it. In fact, it is one of our favorite periods. For the nonce we seem to be in a world all our own, our island floating about in a sea of ice, our cabin thrice cozy and protective.

This year it seemed especially good, with Fiddlesticks and Freckles to share the adventure with us. Loony Coon stayed on the island too. He wasn't much company now, for he was getting so drowsy at the approach of his winter sleep that he dozed most all the time.

We tied new, extra-bright ribbons on our fawns. They apparently understood the ice conditions and made no effort to go away. Fiddlesticks even accepted a dinner of milk from the bottle, though he acted embarrassed about it, and looked around to make sure no stranger could see him.

Then one clear, frosty morning, the season was upon us. I knew what to expect, for I had experienced it before. Giny had not.

"I could never have believed it!" she exclaimed, as we stood watching the dawn unfold and listening to the roll of guns. "Why, it is like a battle! How many hunters do you suppose there are?"

"Last year there were three hundred and fifty thousand licensed deer hunters in Wisconsin. I suppose this year the number is equally large, perhaps larger."

"Three hundred and fifty thousand!" she repeated after me incredulously. "Why, that is an army, and a big army. How many deer did they take?"

"Thirty-five thousand."

"Oh." Giny looked pained. "I know the arguments—that this is necessary or the herd would become too large. I try to be reasonable and tolerant, but—" she pointed to the distant shooting with a sweep of her hand—"how anyone can call such a thing pleasure I don't understand."

I did not reply. I had gone round and round in this argument for years, trying to maintain a position that was wise and practical in spite of my own inclinations. Silence was my only achievement. Within, my thoughts rebelled.

"What was that?" Giny asked, as a sound came suggesting someone struck the cabin with a stone, right below the window where we stood. I went out to investigate. The cause was easily found. There was a bullet half buried in the cottage siding. Some one of those distant guns had fired in our direction, and the bullet, its force largely spent, had found our house!

We heard no more such barrages after the first day of the season. Many hunters had their prizes and departed, making a motley parade down the highway. Deer became more wary. A real cold wave swept into the region, dropping the temperature to near zero. The majority of hunters are not seasoned woodsmen, but inexperienced city people on a lark. They are ill-prepared for the rugged nature of the north. Their camps are frail and they know nothing of woodcraft. Hence, many packed up and headed for home.

The cold quickly thickened the ice of our lake. Freckles and Fiddlesticks found it would bear them up, and they went slipping and skidding over to the mainland. Carrying a long pole on my shoulder for aid in case the ice gave way under me, I followed them. Certain supplies were getting low on the island, and I drove to town. The place was buzzing about various happenings of the hunting season.

On his favorite corner, I found Old Timer. He was in a high pitch of excitement. "Look-ut thet! Look-ut thet!" he yelled, holding up his ragged hat, his finger sticking through a hole in the crown. "I'm through, I tell ye. No more huntin' fer me—not on yer life."

"What's the matter, Old Timer?" I asked.

"Matter? Ain't thet comin' pretty close? That was a bullet thet made that hole, and my head wuz jist one inch lower." Old Timer rubbed the spot on his head where he thought the bullet might have hit.

"Didja hear 'bout the school bus?" he asked.

"No, what about it?"

"Fellow took a shot at it. Said he thought 'twar a deer." Old Timer shook his head and rubbed that spot again.

"No!" I said.

"Yeah—I'm tellin' ye. He saw thet streak o' white paint on th' side of th' bus, an' thought it might mebbe be a tail uva deer. So he ups and shoots!"

"Was anyone hurt?"

"Nope. No children aboard, an' driver was goin' home. But it guv the driver a close un. Forty year ago we'da tarred an' feathered a feller fer thet."

I left Old Timer alternately fingering his hat and rubbing the spot on his head.

There were stories to be heard everywhere. Some were humorous, some pathetic. There were the two men, driving up from a city far to the south on their first hunting trip, who entered the region on the opening day of the season. Selecting a spot, they drove their car off the road, covered the radiator with a blanket because of the cold and with rifles in hand went back into the woods. They walked about for an hour, but saw no deer. Then suddenly they discovered a dark-gray object through the brush. Since the law limited the season to fork-horned bucks, they should have waited until they could determine what kind of animal it was. But they had no time for patience. Taking careful aim, one man shot toward the creature. It did not move. He fired two, three, four shots, and still it was motionless. Sure that they had hit it, they walked up to the object—to find that four bullets had pierced the gray blanket and gone into the radiator of their car! Their hunting was over. The rest of their time and money went into a towing and repair job.

One hunter fell in with a stranger as they both walked through the woods.

"Havin' any luck?" the first asked.

"Nope," said the second.

They walked on together, talking of various things. Finally the first hunter became quite confidential.

"I know how you can get a deer," he said.

"Buck?"

"Nope, doe—but it's a deer."

"Where? How?"

"Well," the man said with a wink, "I got several back in the woods. Got 'em before season. Might let you have one if you pay me for my trouble."

"You'll be well paid, all right. Where are they?"

"Over the hill in a little ravine."

"You're just the man I've been looking for!" said the other.

"You have?"

"Yes, I'm the game warden. You're under arrest for illegal hunting."

Some inexperienced hunters had been lost, and were rescued by wardens and rangers. Farmers lost horses and cattle—cases of mistaken identity. In one case a hunter, dressed in the latest toggery obtainable at fashionable sporting-goods stores, shot a pig. He paid the farmer for it willingly—said he thought it was a deer. In even more sad cases, human beings had been the victims of novice nimrods who shot too quickly and too well.

One long-time resident told me he was sure he saw a mountain lion near our refuge to the north. "Saw it full length, walking on a log," he said. "Took a shot at it."

"Hit it?" I asked, with mixed emotions.

"Nope—don't think I did," he said. "The varmint ran away. I followed, but never saw it again."

Soon after the rifle season was over, winter came in earnest. Icy winds whipped through the barren branches of deciduous trees with a moaning sound, making the evergreen forest sway and dance. The ice thickened to the point where we could drive our car across the lake, and use our boathouse for a garage. Snow fell day after day, until there was over two feet accumulated on the ground.

The remnant of the deer herd moved into the great swamps. Here they yarded, to feed on the major winter food: cedar. Here they would pack the snow down hard, huddle together for warmth when the temperature dropped perhaps to thirty, forty or even fifty below zero, and fight off wolves.

Fiddlesticks and Freckles went with the others. They were seen by a logger far, far back in a swamp, their ribbons distinguishing them from a score of companions. Their lives as independent and individual forest creatures had begun. We had done all we could for them. The hazards still facing them were many, but they were strong, healthy and armed with instinct and the training they had received from Bobette.

Our friends of the north promised they would snowshoe to the yarding place occasionally to see them if possible. This they did on Christmas Day. In the yarding place they counted twenty-one deer, two of them wearing faded red, white and blue ribbons about their necks!

Word of this reached Giny and me by radio, as sort of a Christmas present. We were sailing through tropical waters on the steamship *Lurline*, on our way to Hawaii—and Moke.

XIX

HAWAIIAN HOSPITALITY

THE SEA journey to Hawaii from San Francisco takes four and one-half days, and a lovelier period of rest, relaxation, and travel pleasure could hardly be found. The royal-blue ocean stretches out endlessly, while the pure-white S.S. *Lurline* floats upon it like a swan. Midway in this journey is a point in the ocean which is the farthest from land of any place on earth.

Giny and I were fascinated at the flight of a black-footed albatross which trailed our ship hour after hour. As if by magic, a second bird appeared, and then a third.

"They seem never to flap a wing," Giny observed. "They just glide in great arcs, diving and rising with no effort. They keep up with us. How fast is the *Lurline* going?"

"About eighteen knots an hour," I answered. "But the albatross make greater speed than that. See how that one falls behind, and then easily catches up with us."

"And still not a flap of the wing!" she declared, imitating the flight with a motion of her hand. "It's amazing. How do they do it?"

"That is a question for which there is no complete answer," I said. "Ever since men first sailed the ocean

180

they have been puzzled by the flight of the albatross."

"Well, do they ever really flap? I have been watching for hours and I haven't seen them do so."

"Neither have I. Early sailors built up quite a superstition about them. They thought the birds had supernatural power, that they had discovered some kind of locomotion which gave them free rides. Now naturalists contend that they make short, quick motions which can be detected if you observe closely."

Giny was looking at the soaring creatures with her binoculars. "If they do, it's too fast for me," she declared. "I can't make out the slightest motion."

"Neither can I," I agreed, also studying the birds. "We'll just have to take it for granted that they do flap some way, simply because they must."

These birds trailed the ship through most of our journey and though we watched them often never once did we see them give real substantial flaps of their wings.

During the fourth day of our voyage we were well into tropical waters and we stirred up schools of flying fish. These strange creatures sprayed out to starboard and port, reminding us of the flight of grasshoppers one sees when one walks through a Midwestern prairie.

"They don't flap, either," Giny observed.

"Not supposed to," I answered. "They really don't have wings, but rather elongated fins. And they don't fly like a bird, but rather glide like a plane."

"Where do they get their speed?"

"From swimming. They dart out into the air at a great rate and sometimes fly for four or five hundred feet, even rising high enough to drop on the decks of vessels."

Together with other passengers on our ship, we timed a number of flights by individual fish. Several of them stayed in the air for fifteen seconds, and one of their supreme athletes floated along for twenty-five seconds before he finally dropped into the water.

Life aboard the *Lurline* was one constant round of activities. There were lectures, concerts, entertainments by jovial Hawaiians, deck picnics, games, and hours for resting and dreaming. There were interesting people from various parts of the world, and in the delightful informality of life aboard ship they talked freely of their experiences. The *Lurline* became a little floating world all our own, so joyous in atmosphere that there was regret in our thoughts when we reached the last night at sea. The next morning we would dock at Honolulu, the gateway to many happy adventures in a fantastic land.

Giny was rather silent at dinner this last evening of our sea journey. I could draw from her only monosyllables. Wasn't it a lovely evening? Yes! Did she enjoy the day? Yes. Was her dinner satisfactory? Yes. Would she be pleased to reach Honolulu in the morning? Yes. But her thoughts were far away.

"What is it, dear?" I asked. "Is anything wrong?"

"No—everything is quite all right." She made an effort to smile and take an interest in things about her.

"You're lonesome for the north country, aren't you?" I volunteered.

"Yes, I am—how did you guess?"

"Because I am too."

"It's silly, isn't it—in the midst of all this delightful experience to reach back there?" Giny was apologetic for her feelings.

"No," I replied, emphatically, "I think it is quite normal. In fact I anticipated it, and I have an antidote."

"You have a what?"

"I have an antidote. If you will meet me at our stateroom in an hour, I'll either cure our loneliness or else multiply it until we'll fly home. Is it a date?"

It was, and I went about my preparations. Before we left our Sanctuary I had slipped a number of films of our animals into our suitcases, saying nothing of it to Giny. I knew from many years' experience how we both miss our forest home and our animal friends. I felt sure that not even the charms of Hawaii could entirely prevent this yearning. I borrowed a projector and small screen from the ship's purser, and quickly converted our stateroom into a lecture hall. When Giny came, I showed her motion pictures of our north-woods home. The ones that delighted us both most were those of Fiddlestick, Freckles and Bobette, made the morning when we first saw them.

"Oh, you blessed things!" she exclaimed as her pets came on the screen before her.

"Were they worth all the trouble they gave us?" I asked, knowing the answer.

"It wasn't trouble, it was fun," she insisted. "Right now I wish we were right back there, living in a tent at that deer yard."

"At thirty and forty below zero? Br-r-r-r-r-r-r!"

"Do you suppose they will get through the winter?" she questioned. "The snow, the cold, the wolves, maybe still the panther—the threat seems so great."

"Now listen, young lady," I said in forced sternness. "Fawns grew up in the north country long before you and I had anything to do with them. Thousands of them grow up every year. Fiddlesticks and Freckles are not sissies. They know all the tricks, and their chances are good. We can't smooth all the bumps out of their trail, but we helped them past the worst of them. Now stop worrying."

"And you think we will see them in the spring?"

"Yes." Then I added, "I hope," letting these words be lost in the noise of the projector.

In the gray light of early dawn we had our first sight of Hawaii. There, looking like a cloud at the horizon, was the island of Oahu. The street lights of several shore-line villages were still twinkling. Against stars visible at the western horizon we could see the rugged silhouette of the Koolau mountain range.

"What did you say the name 'Oahu' means?" Giny whispered as we watched the unfolding scene before us.

"It means 'a gathering place,'" I replied.

"And Honolulu?"

"That means 'a place of refuge.'"

"And the word 'Hawaii?'"

"Apparently it has no meaning—it is just a name."

Captain James Cook discovered these islands in 1778, but they are discovered anew by every traveler who comes to them. One can hardly believe that such a delightful spot exists until he actually sees it. Discovery was rampant among the passengers who stood at the railing that morning. "There is Koko Head," one exclaimed, spotting that famous landmark. "Those lights are Honolulu," another said enthusiastically. "Diamond Head!" called another, and the name went all about the ship: "Diamond Head! Diamond Head!"

As the light of day spread over land and sea we saw this promontory which is so conspicuous in the history and geography of Hawaii. Diamond Head is an extinct crater. The early Hawaiians knew it as Leahi, and built many legends about it. In the early part of the nineteenth century, English sailors picked up some shining crystals and thought they were diamonds. They called the place "Diamond Head" and so it has remained ever since, though the stones the sailors found were not diamonds.

Daylight grew stronger, and we saw the famed beach of Waikiki, with Honolulu spread beyond it over the mountainside. Now the greeters came aboard. Tug boats, laden with people and with flowers, came alongside the *Lurline*. There were singers, dancers, instrumentalists, men from the press, from the Chamber of Commerce, from the hotels. Probably nowhere else in the world does a traveler receive such a wholehearted welcome. Hundreds of beautiful flower leis were distributed among the passengers. Giny and I were heaped so high with these garlands we could scarcely breathe. Happiness ran high. This welcome has missed the taint of commercialism. It comes right from the heart.

As we came into Honolulu Harbor and docked at the foot of the famous Aloha Tower, music from the Honolulu band and native singers came up to us. Everywhere there were smiles and the word "Aloha" was on all lips.

"I feel like a queen," said Giny.

"And I like a king," I replied.

"Really, these blessed people could do nothing more for us if we were royalty."

At our hotel the welcome rolled on. The manager and his entire staff were there to call "Aloha," and to greet us with warmth. At a table, beautifully decorated with orchids, anthuriums and other flowers, fresh pineapple juice was served. There were more native musicians. Our attention was drawn particularly to a man who sang songs in the Hawaiian tongue. He looked like a native, his skin a dark bronze, his hair wavy and jet black except for little patches of gray at the temples. His appearance and his singing were so impressive we stood listening for some time. He noted our attention, nodded, and smiled in a most friendly manner.

Then came our supreme greeting. We reached our room to find it filled with flowers and a generous basket of fruit. Our telephone rang. It was long distance— "the island of Maui calling." A moment later a child's voice called so loudly I held the receiver far from my ear, "A-LO-HA!"

"Aloha, Moke, bless your heart! Aloha," I called back.

"A-lo-*ha*" came the voice again.

Soon we were in a hectic exchange of greetings, questions and answers. Alternately Giny and I were on the wire, and on the other end were Moke, Liliana, then Moke and more Moke.

"And how are Ewa and Kimo, Moke?" I asked.

There were a few Hawaiian words that meant nothing to me, and then Liliana came on the phone again.

"Ewa and Kimo are in and out of trouble all the time," said Liliana. "Moke was trying to tell you we have a surprise for you—a big surprise."

But she wouldn't tell us what it was.

Giny and I had a surprise for Moke too and we kept it secret. Before we left the mainland we visited a toy-shop and bought seven animated toy animals. There were two deer, a raccoon, two bears, a squirrel and a skunk. When wound up they would walk in a most natural manner, wagging their heads and tails. We could hardly wait to deliver these to our little friend.

XX

WHACKS AT WAIKIKI

THE TUG on our hearts was very strong to rush over to the island of Maui and see Moke, Liliana, Ewa and Kimo.

"And what do you suppose his *surprise* is?" Giny asked, as we sat in our hotel room on our first evening in Hawaii.

"A bird or a bug, or some other live thing doing something or other," I guessed broadly. "One thing sure, we're not going to find out until we get there."

"Are we going right away?"

In answer I pointed with a sweeping gesture to our camera equipment. There was much to be done before we could visit our little Hawaiian boy. After all, we were in Hawaii to make motion pictures, and every photographer knows that a camera is a dictator of the first order. Friendships, pleasures, comforts and even personal safety are of secondary importance when a picture is to be made.

We learned that things vital to our purpose were happening about the islands. On the beach of Waikiki there were to be water sports, with Hawaiian swimmers performing their remarkable aquatic feats. On the island of Kauai was planned a *hukilau*—a native community fishing party. On the big island of Hawaii, the orchid and volcano island, friends were making special preparations for our photography.

"All this before I can see Moke?" Giny asked disappointedly.

"After this comes Moke," I affirmed.

"Slavedriver!" said Giny.

The next morning we learned that our woodpecker of the north woods, with his drumming on our downspout, was not the only feathered alarm clock. Even before the sun came creeping out of the ocean, laying a path of gold to the eastern horizon, myna birds and doves filled the gentle tropical breeze with their calls. Sleep was impossible. Giny and I arose to watch the coming of day.

Our hotel windows faced in two directions. Looking one way we could see lush flower-filled gardens below us. On the other side lay the famed beach of Waikiki, its long stretch of white sands caressed by the foam-crowned blue waves of the Pacific.

"The first morning in Hawaii," Giny murmured, half to herself. "It could never be less than wonderful! What is it about this place that grips one so?"

"The warm comfort, the sunshine, the flowers, the palm trees," I suggested, but with the realization that I wasn't saying anything adequate or convincing.

"It's more than that," said Giny. "Other places have all those things, yet lack that Hawaiian appeal."

We had breakfast served in our room that morning. The smiling, courteous Chinese-Hawaiian boy who brought it was as refreshing as the sunshine that now filled our room and the fresh ripe pineapple he served.

"Aloha, *kakou*," he said, with good humor that was infectious, using Hawaiian words that mean "Greetings, everybody."

"Aloha, *aikane*," replied Giny, meaning "Greetings, friend."

He grinned from ear to ear, pleased to hear these native words. No doubt Giny's pronunciation was far from pure Hawaiian, but the meaning was just the same.

His name was Bill, he said. At least, that would do for a name. His real name was too long and difficult.

"Some of him Chinese," Bill said, trying to explain. "Some of him Hawaii. Each one bad lone—but both? O-o-o-o-o-o," and he gave up the attempt. "You call him Bill," he said, nodding his head affirmatively. "You call him Bill, I come."

Bill insisted that everything must be just right. He placed the breakfast cart where we could look out the window at Waikiki and watch the early-morning swimmers. He served perfectly without being servile, motivated by a genuine desire for us to be happy.

As Bill left the room, he turned and bowed low, giving a long sentence in Hawaiian. We knew we could not remember it, repeat it, or spell it, so we asked the meaning.

"May your day be filled with happiness Hawaii," he said, then shook his head, indicating the interpretation was not quite accurate, but it would do.

"Mahalo nui," Giny answered, which, however lacking in native pronunciation, conveyed to him the meaning: "Many thanks."

Bill beamed again and left us to our breakfast.

"That may be the thing that distinguishes Hawaii," I said after he was gone. "It is the friendliness, the love that is in the manners and the hearts of these people."

"I believe it is," Giny agreed. "No racial prejudice, no group inferior or superior, no one looking down upon another—why, these people are free of the hatred that is such a burden in many parts of the world."

"And we feel it—in the mental atmosphere if not in the actual air we breathe," I said.

The day went well. Camera opportunities were omnipresent. A strong surf rolled in as the morning advanced and the muscular, bronze swimmers joyously displayed their skills. Soon the water was dotted with outrigger canoes, some flying colorful sails, some paddled by powerful, native canoemen. The outrigger canoe is a direct descendant of the old war canoes of

Hawaii. In the pre-white-man past this kind of craft often measured seventy feet long, and could carry up to eighty warriors. The boat part was a single koa tree log, hollowed out by primitive tools. Parallel to the canoe was the outrigger—a buoyant float of wiliwili wood, connected by arching timbers. This aided in keeping the craft upright and helped in meeting the seas. The early tribesmen went from island to island in these crafts, and perhaps the Polynesians who first settled here arrived in similar canoes.

The outrigger canoes of today range from fifteen to forty feet in length. They are used principally for *play,* a word of meaning in Hawaii. Native paddlers sit at bow and stern and load their craft to capacity with *malihinis.* This is the island name for the stranger, the visitor, the traveler. Under the skillful paddling of Hawaiians the outrigger goes out into the ocean a quarter of a mile or more. Soon it comes in riding the crest of a wave. It is an exciting experience. The paddlers and passengers laugh and scream.

Then came the surfboard exhibitions. This is another sport handed down from the pre-white-man days of Hawaii. Surfboarding in the islands during the primitive days was literally the sport of kings. It is difficult, exacting, and in heavy surf it is hazardous. The native swimmers, as at home in the water as fish, make it look all too easy. Paddling far out to sea, they come riding a wave in a long line, laughing, some singing, calling to one another as if there were nothing to this except to find a free surfboard.

"I wonder if I could do that?" I questioned as my camera recorded the spectacle before us.

"I think you could handle a canoe in the north country better," Giny commented, and her remark seemed to challenge me.

"It certainly looks easy," I persisted.

"Maybe that is because they do it so well."

"I still think I can do it. Maybe I'll try toward evening when photography is done."

"Hope the surf calms down," Giny said, goading me onward though her intentions were to the contrary.

The surf did moderate somewhat toward evening. When our camera work was done for the day, Giny and I took a dip in the ocean. A few outrigger canoes and surfboards still came riding in on each favorable wave. We arranged with two native paddlers to take us for several trips in an outrigger. The rides were thrilling, reminding us of shooting the rapids in a canoe back in our north country. This experience over, Giny decided to take another swim. I walked along the beach.

With no one to protect or guide me, I gravitated toward the surfboards. There were several of them in the sands near the water. One of them was quite different from the others. It was considerably thicker and looked a bit uneven, as though it were handmade. While I stood there, a tall, muscular, bronze young man picked up one of the boards, waded into the water, then launched the thing, riding flat on his stomach. With perfect ease he paddled it with his hands, passing over the incoming waves, making his way to sea. A few moments later he came in riding a wave and obviously having a wonderful time. It all looked so easy.

I glanced again at the surfboard which had interested me. I could picture myself standing, relaxed and graceful, while a big but gentle wave bore me along on one of those thrilling rides. I picked up the surfboard, and was amazed to find how light it was. As I examined it, I heard a voice near me say, "That one is real olo."

I looked around to see the singer whom we had heard in the lobby of the hotel. His hair was wet down with sea water, though the attractive gray patches at the temples were still plain.

"Olo?" I repeated.

"Yes. Olo is the wood of the wiliwili. Most surfboards nowadays are made of koa or breadfruit wood. I like olo better. Anyway, in the old days only the royal families used olo, and when I use it, I feel like a king."

He was easy to meet and interesting to talk to. His name he gave as Hank, saying he adopted that since his real name was too long.

"Hank, you are a wonderful singer," I said. "Mrs. Campbell and I are indebted to you for your songs this morning."

He smiled and said modestly, "I could have done better. It was very noisy for Hawaiian songs."

He talked on about surfboards and surfboarding. The sport reached far back into Hawaiian history, he said. It was once the chief interest of kings. The making of the surfboard was quite a ceremony then. The best of the wiliwili trees were reserved for the purpose. The work of fashioning the board was carried out by crude stone implements. Paint used in the finish came from the ti root, or the kukui root.

"The board you hold was made that way by a very old man I know," he said. "I'm proud of this board."

I often wonder what it is in my mental make-up that leads me to do exactly what I would rather not do. I didn't want to have anything to do with surfboarding, that is, for myself. But I couldn't help it. I had the feeling of being on the side of a steep, ice-covered hill, trying to walk up and all the time slipping down.

"Yes, olo is the best wood for surfboards," Hank was saying. "Ever do any surfboarding?"

"Never," I said. "Is it hard to learn?"

"Well—it is one of those things you don't learn. Like parachuting, you just do it. No one can tell you much about it. Do you swim?"

"Some."

"Well, if you wish, take that out and try it. Don't go far the first time, until you feel your balance."

"Think I will," I said bravely, though I was hoping an officer would come up that moment to tell me I had committed some breach of law and must go to jail.

The friendly Hank told me a few things he thought would be helpful in this first venture of mine. I said *yes* to all his advice, but really didn't comprehend a thing. With a feeling of reluctance I carried the light olo board until the water was about knee-deep. Hank was calling something to me, but the sound of the surf drowned out his voice. I placed the board in the water and climbed on it, stretching myself out as I had seen the others do, lying on my stomach. I had just barely got fixed when a big wave broke near me, picking the board up and carrying it far toward the beach, ultimately turning it upside down with me under it, rolling me over and over in the sand. Hank came to my aid, laughing unsympathetically, lifted the board off me and helped me to my feet.

"I was calling to you to go farther out before you mounted the board," he said. "Get beyond the place where the waves break or they will roll you over."

"So I discovered," I said, digging sand out of my hair, eyes, and ears. "Maybe you had better put the board away now."

"No, no—use it all you want. Now go farther out."

With much less enthusiasm than at first I went farther out. My take-off was more successful, if that is the right word. I got aboard the thing and, stretched out on my stomach, I began paddling to sea as I saw others doing. One surfboard paddled by a native swimmer passed me as if I were standing still. "Come on out," this paddler called to me, observing that I was just about to turn and head for shore. "It's no fun here; come on out."

"Thanks," I called back, but I didn't mean it. The farther out I went the smaller that board felt. It tilted and rocked in the waves, and I clung to it with everything but my teeth—and perhaps I used them; I couldn't be sure.

"Here comes a beauty," called the swimmer, pointing to a wave that appeared about the size and shape of the Rocky Mountains. "Get ready."

I got ready the best I knew how. Aping the others, I pointed my olo raft toward land. It was where I wanted to go, but I doubted if I would ever reach it. Here came that wave, like a thing alive. It danced and foamed, and I am sure it roared. I and my craft seemed to grow smaller and smaller in comparison, until I felt like a second in the path of centuries.

"Paddle!" yelled the delighted Hawaiian near me. "Give it all you've got. *Wahoo-o-o-o!*"

I gave it all I had, which wasn't much. The wave was upon me. It picked me up as if I were a feather, and a very little feather at that. Away the olo board and I went, I felt sure at a speed of a hundred miles or more, though local people insist that this surf travels at only thirty miles an hour.

My swimmer friend was wild with joy. His face covered with one great smile, he stood up on his surf-board like a circus rider. I was still lying flat down and wondering how long I could continue to do that.

"Up!" he screamed. "Don't miss this. You don't see a wave like this often."

I had no breath to reply, but if I had had I would have said something to the effect that I would rather never see another wave, and if I could get rid of this one in some magic way, I would do so. Nevertheless, I tried to get up—first on one knee, then on the other, my hands gripping the sides of the board, all the while praying that I be spared what I felt was before me.

"Up!" roared my merciless companion.

Apprehensively I let go with my hands, trying to balance myself on that swaying board beneath me. Just then the great wave started doing tricks. I saw my adviser go tumbling from his board and into the surf— still laughing. And who was I to ride a wave even experts couldn't master? My olo board suddenly stood on its nose, and I went head-first into that seething sea. Really, it was quite a relief to do so. I wasn't afraid of the water, knowing that I could swim to shore, and I

would far rather do it on my own than play around with that flippant and fun-loving surfboard. I took in a breath as I went down, gave several strokes underwater and then came to the surface. As I did, I met my surfboard again. It was coming down as I came up—and it landed right on my head! The owner on the beach had told me how light olo was, but it didn't feel that way to me. My senses were swimming and I was too. Somehow I got ashore where I furnished a great deal of amusement for a gathering crowd, including a giggling Giny.

"I meant to tell you that if you get thrown off, you should swim underwater a way so the board won't hit you," said Hank, having retrieved his olo board. He looked first at the board to see if it were split, and then at my head with the same thought in mind.

"I guess I'll know better next time," I said, secretly vowing there would be no next time.

In our room Giny examined the bulging knot on my head. "You couldn't wear a hat," she commented and then added with an aggravating smile, "Never mind—people don't wear hats in Hawaii anyway."

XXI

A NATIVE HUKILAU

WHILE the bump (totally unrelated to knowledge) slowly subsided, we photographed many of the glories of Oahu. With the able assistance of one of Hawaii's best photographers and the co-operation of the weather, we gathered into our camera a harvest of beauty. The endless pineapple fields with their luscious fruit, the sugar-cane fields topped with plumes looking like pampas grass, the rugged Koolau mountain range, the famous Nuuanu Pali (cliff), the Nuuanu Valley, Pearl Harbor, the beaches, the magnificent temples—all presented a bewildering array of picture opportunities.

Oahu is the third island in size in the Hawaiian group. It has 604 square miles of interesting and beautiful tropical scenery. The city of Honolulu, with its population of nearly 300,000, has nearly half the people of the islands. Historic Pearl Harbor, home of the United States Pacific Fleet, is suburban to Honolulu.

We talked to Moke several times. His affections were now transferred from the mailman to the telephone, and he would seldom permit himself to be where he could not hear it ring. When it did ring, he always got there first, and accused whoever called of being "Kam and Geenee." His loud A-lo-*ha* was refreshing to hear. Each conversation brought new reference to his *surprise* and he giggled happily at our anxiety to know what it was.

Giny told Moke as much as she could of my adventure with a surfboard. He was especially interested by her description of the bump on my head. He had had bumps on his own little head, but he had never had one "the size of an egg," as Giny described mine. He wanted to know what kind of an egg. If it was like the egg of an iiwi bird, that didn't amount to much. But if it resembled a chicken egg—that was wonderful! So Giny described my now famous bump as this latter variety.

Moke insisted that I keep the bump so he could see it.

"We must keep it large," Giny said, looking at me significantly. "You wouldn't want to disappoint Moke, would you? Let's see . . . to keep that the right size I could use a hammer, a war club or . . ."

"A surfboard?" I put in.

"Yes, a good idea," she said enthusiastically. "How about a repeat performance with the surfboard? That should have been photographed anyway—and this time I can have the camera all ready."

Later, on the beach, she suggested this to Hank. He was all for it, and generously or threateningly offered me the use of his surfboard. Others took an interest in my further discomfort too, and it became quite the thing along Waikiki to ask when this next exhibition of how *not* to ride a surfboard was going to occur.

I used every excuse I could think of to keep from giving my merciless friends this barbarous bit of amusement. When these were exhausted, I conveniently arranged for us to depart for the island of Kauai.

Blessed Kauai! What a wealth of primitive charm is concentrated in this garden spot of 555 square miles! It is the fourth island in size in the Hawaiian archipelago, but it has more than its proportionate share of native loveliness and friendliness. Giny and I rate it our favorite of the islands. Both Oahu and Hawaii have what may be called growing pains of a kind. The cities are expanding rapidly, and a bit of the hurry, rush and sophistication of the mainland is creeping in. But on Kauai old Hawaii lives on.

It took our plane forty minutes to get from the Honolulu airport to Lihue, largest city on Kauai. Here we were greeted by Kamuela, a pure-blooded Hawaiian whom we had learned to know and love on our previous visit. His greeting was of such warmth and friendliness as to relieve us of any feeling that we were strangers.

"Aloha! Aloha!" he called, as we stepped off the plane. "Aloha, *nui, nui.*" And he bestowed the traditional Hawaiian kiss on Giny's cheeks. For me he had a handshake of such sincerity and strength my fingers ached when it was done.

"How good to see you again!" said Giny.

"I have been counting the days until you came," replied Kamuela, bowing low.

Kamuela was our guide, and a more efficient one we could not wish for, nor could we find a more pleasant companion. We knew from previous experience his love for his island home and his knowledge of every nook and corner. We knew, too, that in his car he carried his ukulele, and that we might expect it to be used frequently as an accompaniment for his rich voice and native songs.

Kamuela took us first to the Kauai Inn, which would be our headquarters during our stay on this island. Here we were greeted by Mike, Bob, Hiram and others—Hawaiian boys whom we already knew.

"And do you see who is over there under that coconut palm?" Giny directed my attention to a man standing a short distance away. He was very dark, like a native, of powerful build and neatly dressed.

"Don't you recognize your surfboard instructor?" laughed Giny. "It's Hank!"

"Hank!" I called. He smiled and gave a salute as a greeting. "Come on over here—and I hope you don't have your surfboard along."

"No, you're safe," he said, walking toward us. He was well acquainted with all the boys who stood about.

"Hank shows up here about once a month," said

Kamuela. "Just pops in unannounced and then pops out again."

"Comes to give us a singing lesson," said Mike, himself a splendid tenor.

"Rather I come here to get one," replied Hank.

"This your home island, Hank?" I asked.

"No," he said, with a shake of his head.

"Family or relatives here?"

There was another brief "No," then feeling something more needed to be said, he added, "I have a vacation now and—well, I just *have* to come to Kauai once in a while."

He looked away and his face sobered. I had the feeling that he did not want me to press him further about the reason for his visits, so I changed the subject and got all the boys to suggest subjects for me to photograph.

What marvels this island of Kauai has to offer! Rugged mountain ranges that knife their way into the sky, valleys of tropical charm, vistas of coastal views that stagger thought, waterfalls, rivers—Kamuela led us from one gorgeous sight to another. Kalalau Lookout, the Napali Cliffs, Opaikaa Valley, Hanalei Bay, the Waimea Canyon that resembles the Grand Canyon of Arizona—we couldn't pronounce all the names but we could admire the beauty.

Even Mount Waialeale posed for a picture. This was quite a concession, for Waialeale is about the wettest mountain in the world, and usually wears concealing garments of clouds. The average rainfall on this peak is 460 inches a year. The all-time record for a twelve-month period is 624 inches, and this is fifty-two feet of water! When we saw Waialeale standing out sharp and clear in the morning sun, we were much astonished and took our pictures quickly. It was well we did, for thirty minutes later a great cloud had swallowed up the mountain.

One of the most beautiful experiences possible in these islands is the boat trip up the Wailua River to the Fern Grotto. The Wailua River is the only navigable fresh-water river in all Hawaii. It winds its way through palm-lined banks, small mountains rising at either side, giving a visitor the impression that he is penetrating a tropical jungle. The route is rich in historic spots and Hawaiian traditions. The Fern Grotto is a wide, shallow cave, the walls of which are festooned with soft, lacy ferns.

The day Giny and I were to photograph this, we noticed a strange twinkle in the eyes of our friends at Kauai Inn. They helped us load our camera equipment in the car.

"Everything all set?" Kamuela asked of Mike, and I noticed a wink.

"All set!" said Mike, and he winked back.

Hank, Bob, Hiram and Harry came up to see us off, all wearing smiles that indicated something was afoot.

"You're going to show Sam and Giny our African tulip tree, aren't you?" Hank asked of Kamuela.

I protested that we had already photographed a tulip tree, but Kamuela took us to see this special one anyway. I had the feeling he was only using up time.

At the Wailua River a boat was waiting for us. The day was clear and lovely, and the winding river reflected the deep blue of the sky. We arrived at the Fern Grotto when the sun was just right for pictures. The cave is surrounded by dense growth and twilight reigns there except for a brief period in early afternoon. Kamuela appeared quite nervous. He tried to be casual, but he kept looking anxiously at the high rock cliffs above the mouth of the cave.

Suddenly Giny caught my arm. "Listen," she said, directing my attention above. I could hear the soft strumming of ukuleles and guitars. Then a man's voice began the enchanting strains of the "Wedding Song," one of the most beautiful duets in Hawaii's lovely folklore of music. Soon a woman's voice joined, the blending of the two voices and the stringed instruments saturating the air with harmony. Giny and I listened enchanted. It was more than mere music we heard that day. It was the spirit of these blessed people, the beauty of the islands, the romantic atmosphere, the traditional friendliness, all gathered into sound and rhythm.

Soon the singers and players advanced to a ledge above us where we could see them. Hank was the man singer and the woman with the beautiful voice was one named Leilani. Mike, Bob, Hiram and Harry furnished the background music on ukuleles and guitars. The lovely surroundings, the spirit which prompted these fine people to do this for Giny and me, the artistry with which it was carried out—all combined to make this one of the sweetest experiences we have ever known.

"Nice of you to stop at that tulip tree," said Hank, after we had thanked them all for this precious gift. "Otherwise, we couldn't have beaten you here."

The next morning Kamuela called for us early. He was about as excited as he ever gets. News had reached him that a *hukilau* was to be staged at a near-by beach. Watchers on a hill had noted those signs which indicate that a school of fish is at hand. They saw those strange birds, the men-o'-war, circling, dipping and diving in an area of the sea. Here in the waters was what appeared to be a great, subsurface shadow, moving slowly toward land. Word spread rapidly through the community that there were fish offshore. It was time for the *hukilau!* Get out the nets! Everyone come and give a hand!

When we arrived, they were already placing their great net, an eighth of a mile long, about the school of fish. Now many willing hands grasped the ropes of the net and began pulling it into shore. The rules of the *hukilau* are that anyone who aids in any way with this work is entitled to a share of the fish. We set up our camera at a vantage point, and began recording this event.

"Sam, there's Hank!" Giny pointed my attention to our new friend. "Isn't he having a wonderful time?"

Hank was. He was into everything, pulling on the net and at times dashing into the sea to swim out and loosen the bottom as it got caught on rocks or logs. Sighting us, he waved an aloha and then with boyish enthusiasm raced into the ocean again.

On came the net under the strong, steady pull of two-score native people. When it reached the shore, cries of triumph went up. It was a wonderful catch and everyone was happy. While the young people laughed, shouted and danced, the older ones sang a few strains of some old-time chant.

"There will be a feast tonight," exclaimed Kamuela, joyous as the others at the successful *hukilau*. "Would you two like to come?"

"What will the feast consist of?" I asked, a bit apprehensive.

"Raw fish and poi."

"Ugh!" Giny winced.

"Kamuela," I said, placing my hand on his arm. "You'll understand, won't you, if I say we have a previous engagement."

Kamuela understood and smiled.

Late one day we were driving along the beautiful road that follows the southwest coast of Kauai. Our photography of this island was finished and the next

day we planned to move on to other fields. We passed
Waimea Bay, the first place Captain Cook landed when
he discovered the islands. Kamuela stopped our car at
a point where we could see Niihau Island, seventeen
miles away. The rays of the setting sun were touching
it and we could see it plainly on the distant horizon.

"You know about Niihau?" asked Kamuela.

"A little," I said. "It is privately owned, is it not?"

"Yes, and the people who own it seem to want to save
a little of old Hawaii. Real Hawaiian people live there
much as we all used to live. If they come off the island,
they are not permitted to return—that is, except under
certain conditions."

"How many native people are over there?"

"Only about three hundred."

"And they like their little world?"

"Yes, they do. I know some of them. They speak the
pure Hawaiian language."

"You have been there?"

"Yes—but not often." Kamuela was looking on down
our shore toward a rocky point. "Look," he said, pointing that way. "He is there—I knew he would be."

"Who is it?" asked Giny, studying a figure indistinct
in the distance.

"Hank," said Kamuela. "That's his favorite spot,
where he can sit and look at Niihau. He was born
there, and lived there through his boyhood. Then he
got the desire to see the outside world. You know—the

call of cities, excitement, distant places—and he left, knowing that he would never be allowed to return."

"Kamuela," I said, "is that what brings him to Kauai regularly? Does he long to go back to Niihau?"

"So badly that he suffers," said Kamuela, showing the sympathy he felt. "He sits there and looks at the distant shore for hours. I have seen him sit through a hard rainstorm and never take his eyes off that island. He found he didn't fit in the world, I guess."

We did not disturb Hank's solitude, but drove on, leaving him gazing dreamily at his loved Niihau. That evening I found him in the lobby at Kauai Inn. The joy we had seen in him at the *hukilau* was lacking, and he looked heavy of heart. I tried to draw him into conversation, thinking I might help him, but he hid behind monosyllables.

A letter reached us from Ada and Ray back in Wisconsin. It was disturbing. Ever since we left the north country it had been snowing, the letter said, and a great accumulation was on the ground. Drifts were high at the roadside. The blanket of snow was soft, giving a distinct advantage to wolves. Because of their snowshoelike feet they could go over the surface, while the sharp hoofs of deer sank in deeply. Our friends were striving to keep in touch with the deer yard where Fiddlesticks and Freckles were, but even on snowshoes they had difficulty getting there.

The most distressing part of the report concerned the

food situation. The range of the deer was being narrowed greatly by snow conditions. Only a few white cedars, principal winter food, were within reach. These seemed insufficient to last the deer until spring. Our friends were working with the conservation warden to take food to the animals, but getting it to the valley was a problem.

We talked to Moke and Liliana that night. Moke wanted to send our deer some poi. He said it was good for them.

XXII

SURPRISE!

OUR WORK on Kauai finished, we flew to the island of Hawaii. Hawaii is at the southeastern extremity of the group. It is often called "The Big Island," as it is almost twice the size of all other islands combined, having 4,030 square miles. Other names are "The Orchid Isle," and "The Volcano Island." Here we experienced more days of exciting adventure, photographing the orchid gardens of Hilo, the Black Sands of Kalapana, the tree-fern forest, the steam vents of the Kilauea Crater, the Halemaumau Fire Pit, the towering peaks of Mauna Loa and Mauna Kea, the ancient City of Refuge, the quaint native towns. All these gave our camera plenty to do.

Then came the day we boarded a plane for the island of Maui—and Moke. The shores of Hawaii and Maui are only twenty-seven miles apart. On each we could see the great, irregular black areas that are lava flows of the past. Some of these are centuries old.

Our pilot took us over the crater of Haleakala, whose name means "House of the Sun." This is the world's largest dormant volcano. Its highest point is 10,025 feet above sea level, its rugged crater seven miles long and two miles wide. Inside this crater grows the oddly beautiful silver-sword plant, found only in Hawaii and certain places in the Himalaya Mountains.

In a very few minutes our plane glided into the airport of Kahului, near Wailuku, largest town on Maui. As we walked toward the gate, carrying our box of toy animals, we could hear an excited little voice crying, "Alo*ha*! Alo*ha*!"

"Aloha, Moke, aloha!" Giny and I called in unison, discovering our precious little friend among the waiting crowd.

It is against the rules for anyone except passengers to come out on the airfield, but Moke was in no mood to be governed by rules. Breaking from his mother's hand and slipping right through the legs of the guard, he came running to us so fast he almost left his feet behind. In his hands he held two orchid leis so long they trailed on the ground. The inevitable happened. He stepped on the end of a lei, and fell flat. The flowers suffered more from the fall than he did, and he literally bounced to his feet, running on with what was left of the leis. He kept right on running even after he was in Giny's arms, and she had a hard time holding the exuberant child.

Scarcely knowing what he was saying, he kept spilling alohas all over the place. In his excited talk he had English and Hawaiian words so tangled we knew little of what he was saying, but we did make out "Ewa," "Kimo," and "surprise." Finally he placed the tattered leis on our necks, accompanied by traditional Hawaiian kisses given in an extra-cute way.

Giny carried Moke to the gate. She had no choice. He locked his arms around her neck and held on tight as a tick. As we passed the guard, he poked a dimple in Moke's cheek, saying, "You broke the law, young fellow. I'd put you in jail if I had a cell your size."

Moke flashed back that smile of his that made the guard his prisoner immediately.

Liliana's greeting was more restrained and dignified than Moke's, but none the less loving. "I believe I can comprehend the length of eternity now," she said, joining Moke in Giny's embrace. "It is that period in between the time the Campbells say they are coming and when they arrive."

Giny and I stared at her. It seemed to us she was even more beautiful than we remembered her. In her jet-black hair she wore an orange-colored hybiscus. Her dark eyes danced with enthusiasm, and her continuous parade of smiles brought glimpses of perfect white teeth.

Liliana led us to the parking area, where her car had been left. Moke released his hold on Giny under the constant pleading of his mother, but he insisted on walking between us where he could hold tightly to one of my fingers with one hand and to Giny's with the other. With that keen childish intuition that recognizes its own, he eyed the box of toys I carried. We let him speculate, figuring that anticipation was good for him.

"My jalopy doesn't look very good but don't be afraid of it," said Liliana, as we approached an automobile that reflected years of service. "It runs well and my good neighbors keep it in good mechanical condition for me. We must make it last a little while longer."

"It looks good to us, Liliana," I said. "We like old cars—get very attached to them."

"We like Kamehameha," she said, looking at the car affectionately. It was named after the hero king of the islands. "He conquers everything—hills, mud roads, sands, distance. We couldn't get along without our Kamehameha."

"Are Ewa and Kimo in Kamehameha?" I asked, looking through the car windows.

"No, though they usually are," Liliana answered. "We left them in the house, because we have planned to keep you out all day and they wouldn't be happy in the car for so long a time. You'll see them late this afternoon—and you'll see our surprise too."

Moke was tugging at his mother's hand, seeking attention. She bent low while he whispered something in her ear. She whispered back, and Moke listened, turning a telltale gaze on the box I carried. He said something more, and she replied, ending with an admonition, "Please now, dear, you do as Mother says." Moke glanced at the box again but said nothing. I winked at Giny.

"Please pardon this private family conversation," Liliana said to us. "Now about the day: we thought we would go up to the Iao Valley from here. That is right near Wailuku, and is one of the most beautiful spots on Maui."

"Wonderful! Giny and I love that valley," I said. "But I have one little request. Is there a quiet place where we could go for a few minutes? We have a matter to take up with Moke."

"Why, yes," Liliana replied. "There is a little picnic grounds at the entrance of Iao Valley. Some tables are there, and I have a picnic lunch. It's near noon, and I thought we would stop there before we go up the valley."

The spot proved to be just what we wanted. While Liliana unwrapped and spread a wonderful lunch, Moke was presented with the mysterious box. Amid happy Hawaiian squeals, he took out the toy animals. He named them at once after animal characters in my books. The raccoon was Loony Coon, the two deer were Fiddlesticks and Freckles, the bears were Bunny Hunch and Big Boy, the squirrel was Eeny, and the skunk was Zinnia. He kept Giny and me busy winding them up, to keep all hopping and skipping around the picnic table. He tried to feed the miniature Fiddlesticks and Freckles, remembering the report that they might be

hungry. He said, "Thank you" in English, and *"Mahalo"* in Hawaiian. But his happy little laughter as he watched the toys perform was the best *thank you* of all.

After lunch, we drove up Iao Valley to magnificent scenery and an unexpected adventure. The valley was a constant unfolding of beauty. The mountains that rise at either side are a mass of forests. The Iao creek leaps over waterfalls and races over rapids on its journey to the sea. The road penetrates the valley part way, and from its end a trail leads on. Back in here stands the Iao Needle, a spire 2,200 feet high. As we directed our camera to this subject, I heard a voice calling from a cliff above us, "Aloha! Sam and Giny!"

On looking up, we saw our friend Hank standing on a rock waving to us. "Aloha," he called again. "Are you following me or am I following you?"

We called him down to meet Liliana and Moke.

"Liliana!" He repeated her name as they shook hands. "I've seen you before somewhere, haven't I?"

"You look very familiar to me, too," she replied, flashing one of her prettiest smiles. "Perhaps we have met."

"I know," Hank said, his eyes lighting up. "On Lei Day in Honolulu. You sang at the festival, remember?"

"That's it!" Liliana agreed. "You sang there too. You sang beautifully."

"You were wonderful." Hank was enthusiastic, still continuing the handshake. "Such a lovely voice! Why have I not heard you again? Do you still sing?"

"Only for him." She indicated Moke. "He is my whole life right now."

"Oh, but you must sing—publicly—for everybody," Hank insisted. "You have no right to hide such a voice."

The two suddenly remembered that we were there and with apologies turned their thoughts again to our photography. We went on up the trail, Moke riding on Hank's wide shoulders.

The afternoon hours went all too fast. The shadows grew long and picture taking was done for the day. Liliana asked Hank to join us again the next day when we were going for an all-day trip to the summit of Haleakala.

"Will I?" he said. "Don't ask me unless you mean it."

She did mean it, and we all joined in urging that he go with us. Moke was especially insistent. He had taken quite a fancy to Hank. We fixed a meeting place for the next day. Hank drove back to Wailuku in a car he had rented, while we drove to Liliana's home at Lahaina in the rattling-good Kamehameha.

Liliana had engaged a cabin for us near her home. It was clean, attractively furnished and so situated that we could see out over the ocean from our windows. She helped us move in, and Moke did his part too. Then she invited us over to her home, a hundred yards away, saying, "You may see the *surprise*."

As we got out of the car, we heard a voice like that of a teenager calling in a very saucy manner. It sounded close at hand and apparently the words were directed at us.

"Hi, wise guy," said the voice. I felt a wave of resentment sweep through me. Discourtesy is such a sad mark of ignorance I dislike to see it in anyone, especially young people. This was particularly offensive, for it was so unexpected. Back in the busy cities of the mainland bad manners often crop out, owing perhaps to the unnatural pace of life there. But here in Hawaii such an affront was decidedly out of place.

However, there was no mistake about it, the words were said and they were meant for me. "Hi, wise guy" came the irritating call again. I tried to ignore it, but it persisted. "Wise guy. Think you're smart, eh?"

Angry in spite of myself, I looked about for the offender. "Wise guy, wise guy, smart guy," the voice went on. I looked at the windows of the house to see if all this came from there.

"Look up in the tree," Liliana suggested. She and Moke were laughing at my discomfort.

I did—just as a myna bird came hopping down a limb and looked down at me. "Wise guy," the bird cried with perfect diction. "Wise guy, smart guy, eh?"

"Surprise!" Moke clapped his hands. "Surprise!"

I looked at Liliana for explanation. "Yes," she said, still greatly amused, "that is the surprise—and his name

is *Surprise*. Moke could hardly wait for you to see him. Friends who were moving away gave him to us. He isn't very polite, but he's lots of fun—and he doesn't know what he is saying."

"Well, Surprise, you old rascal!" I exclaimed. "How about coming down here while I teach you some manners?"

"Surprise, you're much too pretty to say such awful things." Giny held out her hand to him.

"Oh, wise guy, eh?" said Surprise.

Moke was out of the car now and the myna flew right up and perched on his head. "Smart guy," Moke said, mimicking the tone the bird used.

"Smart guy," the bird repeated.

I stood there feeling very foolish.

"Our friends made such a pet of him," Liliana explained. "They taught him those awful things, and they could have taught him something nice just as well."

"Well, no matter what he says, he just means 'hello,' " Giny declared.

"That's all," Liliana agreed. "And knowing that, we just hear a greeting regardless of his words. He insulted our neighbors when he first came, but they're used to him now. Really, he is a dear. Now come on, you must meet Ewa and Kimo."

Now we came to a second surprise, one that nearly brought tears to the stouthearted Moke. Ewa was there, but Kimo was gone! A newly made hole in the bottom of the screen door told the story of his escape.

XXIII

SPECTRE OF THE BROCKEN

THERE WAS a frantic search for Kimo during the evening. Moke called and called until his little voice cracked. Ewa was obviously a very much disturbed hen, and she called too, as if to a brood of chicks. Liliana went to the neighbors, fearful lest Kimo had invaded their land and invoked the waiting shotgun. They had not seen him.

Giny and I walked about calling, "Kimo!" We looked behind trees, under buildings, and in brush, not knowing much what to do but wanting to do something. We recalled similar situations back in the north woods when we had searched for Fiddlesticks and Freckles, and we sympathized with Moke. Kimo had had a ribbon and a bell on his neck when last seen, so we used our ears as well as our eyes in seeking him. Darkness put an end to our search, and Kimo had not been found.

Our Hawaiian boy took Ewa to bed with him that night, but he was a pretty disconsolate little fellow. For months he had planned this evening when Giny and I would see Kimo and Ewa together. It was rather hard to swallow the disappointment.

The searching and calling were resumed the next morning, but Kimo remained an absentee. Moke would hardly eat his breakfast. When it came time to leave for Haleakala, he was reluctant to go. Only the thought of seeing Hank kept him from being an out-and-out rebel. He took his toy animals along.

When we joined with Hank, Moke quickly monopolized his attention. Kimo was gone, he said; we couldn't find Kimo anywhere. Hank sensed it was a pretty sad situation, and he took it upon himself to administer consolation and help.

"Now, now, Moke," he said, taking the boy in his arms. "Kimo will come back. We will find him."

"Mahea?" Moke said in a thin voice, using the Hawaiian word for "where."

"Where? Oh, we'll find him wherever he is—in the sea, in the woods, on the moon if we have to." And he tossed Moke high above his head.

The boy seemed satisfied with the promise and his happy disposition returned. He laughed and played with Hank.

"He has confidence in you, Hank," I said. "You'll have to make good now and find Kimo."

"I'll surely do my best, but I have to ask, who or what is Kimo?"

Hank had never heard of Kimo and Ewa, and had no idea what they were. He knew only that Moke wanted Kimo.

"What you have done is promise to find a pet mongoose."

"A pet mongoose?" Hank gasped, putting his hand to his head. "I never heard of such a thing. Well—if Moke wants Kimo, we'll find Kimo even if he is a mongoose."

The day went wonderfully well. Haleakala was free of clouds and this does not happen often. We drove to the summit, stopping frequently along the way. From the 10,000-foot elevation we could see the island of Hawaii plainly and the endless blue ocean. Hank proved to be a splendid assistant cameraman, familiar with exposures, focus and composition. He insisted on carrying a disproportionate share of the equipment. Moke, in imitation, carried our binocular case.

We went some distance down one of the trails leading into the crater, there to photograph the silver sword. We found a beautiful specimen of this fascinating plant. There were fully a hundred of the silver-colored slender leaves.

"It really looks artificial," Liliana said, stooping to look closely at the fantastic plant.

"Yes—more like something made to decorate a Christmas tree than a growing thing," Giny added.

"Some time you should go to the bottom of the crater," Hank put in. "You need several days to do it but it is marvelous down there. I have stayed there for a week. The silver swords are larger there. I have seen them almost as tall as I."

I was beginning to realize there wasn't much about Hawaii this boy had not seen. He knew the history, the botany, the geography and the legends of this land, and his knowledge was furthered by an all-consuming love of the islands.

Mists were gathering in the crater and Hank thought it best we go back up the trail. Trails can be lost in these low clouds and the way become hazardous. Moke rode up the steep climb on Hank's shoulders, curling his legs about the man's muscular neck and hanging on to his hair for support.

"Wikiwiki! Wikiwiki!" cried Moke, using the word for "hurry."

Hank tried to *wikiwiki,* but the trail was too steep for speed, even for an athlete like him.

By the time we reached the summit, the crater was filled with soft, cotton clouds. We paused to rest, not knowing that we were soon to look upon a spectacle that few have seen. The sun was getting low in the west. Liliana and Giny walked to the edge of the crater and looked in. Hank sat down on a rock and took Moke in his lap. I was cleaning the mist from the lenses of my camera.

"You know, Sam, I love to look into this boy's eyes," Hank said, chucking the youngster under the chin. "It gives me the same sensation I get when I look at Niihau. There is much of old Hawaii there: *hukilaus,* surfrid-

ing, outriggers, palm trees, the carefree happiness of
tribal days—it's all there right in those eyes. This boy
is Hawaii."

"Then, Hank, it isn't a place you yearn for, or a
time—it's a state of mind." I had been wanting to say
this to our friend, and this seemed to be the right moment.

"Would you say that again?" he asked, looking at me
a little startled.

I repeated the sentence and then added, "If it's a
place you cannot reach, or a time you cannot recall, that
you think is necessary to your happiness—don't you see
you are in a hopeless position? But if it is just a state of
mind, a condition of thought within yourself that needs
adjustment, then it lies within your power of accom-
plishment."

He stared at me for a moment thinking. "You know,
Sam, you have given me something," he said earnestly.
"If Moke can make me feel the way Niihau does, then
it must be something that is in me—merely stimulated,
merely awakened. I can't say just what I feel, can't find
right words, but——"

"Sam, Sam," Giny called, "come here quickly. You
never saw such a sight."

We hurried over to where the two women stood staring down into the crater. Looking down, we beheld an
amazing sight—the complete circle of a rainbow!

"The Spectre of the Brocken," Hank gasped.

"The Spectre of the Brocken," Liliana repeated, entranced.

"Spec-a-Brock!" chimed in Moke, not knowing what to call this amazing scene but as charmed as we were.

Truly it was the famed Spectre of the Brocken, and it hardly seemed fair that we should view it on such a brief, casual visit to Haleakala. Travelers have come to this place scores of times without seeing it, and some

natives have lived on Maui a lifetime without this experience. It is the complete rainbow created by the reflection of sunlight, when all conditions are just right. Our own images were etched on the clouds at the very center of the rainbow. Tradition has it that such a spectacle may be seen only one other place in the world: from the Brocken peak in the Harz Mountains of Germany.

Hank had seen it once before he said, from down in the crater. Liliana had never seen it, and of course neither had we. Moke declared he had seen it *many* times, and who were we to argue with a boy's imagination?

Hank couldn't let him get away with the statement, however, and, giving the youngster a pat on the back, he said, *"Hoomalimali"*—which is the Hawaiian way of saying, "hooey," or "bunk."

The Spectre of the Brocken faded out as suddenly as it began. The sun sank low and the rainbow disappeared. We walked away from the rim in silence, quite overcome with what we had seen. Then suddenly Giny spoke. "Sam—your camera! You didn't take a picture of that!"

She stared at me with a look that was compounded of pity and disgust. I said nothing, for there wasn't anything to say.

We arrived at Liliana's home in early evening. Hank drove over with us, using the excuse that he had promised Moke to find Kimo. Once there, he and Moke wandered casually about the grounds, looking in the same places we had looked the previous evening and morning.

Presently we heard them coming back, Moke calling excitedly for his mother. As they approached, we saw the boy had an animal in his arms.

"Kimo!" he cried. "Kimo!"

In a moment we were circled about him, looking at Kimo, who nestled contentedly in his embrace. Kimo had several cuts about his face, but otherwise looked like a very happy animal.

"Kimo is a hero," Hank said, "and he deserves the best."

"Where did you find him, and what has he done to get these cuts?" asked Liliana.

"He was over at the neighbor's." Hank indicated the house where the chickens were.

"Not after their chickens, I hope," Liliana said anxiously.

"No," Hank said, scratching about Kimo's ears. "In fact, he *saved* the chickens. About an hour ago your neighbor looked out and saw a mongoose approaching his chicken coop. He went back in for his gun, and when he came out, he saw a second mongoose approaching. This one had a ribbon and a bell on his neck, and he knew it must be your pet, Kimo. The first mongoose made a dash for a chicken, and as he did Kimo here charged him. There was a fierce fight, but Kimo did away with the enemy and saved the chicken. Kimo was hurt a little and pretty tired. Your neighbor picked him up and kept him until he saw us. So—Kimo is a hero!"

No hero ever received more caresses and pats than did Kimo. Each one of us had to take him in our arms and tell him how wonderful he was. Then Moke took him to find Ewa, and to show her that all was well. Ewa was roosting in a low bush and didn't care much about being disturbed. She did stir herself as she saw Kimo, however, and stretched her neck in his direction, talking chickenese. Kimo stretched his nose toward her and sniffed. As he did, she reached forward and gave him one good peck!

Moke slept well that night—with Kimo and Ewa.

XXIV

MIND YOUR OWN BUSINESS

KIMO AND Ewa strolled around the grounds together the morning after his big battle, and Moke went with them. The companionship of those two strange creatures and the little Hawaiian boy was something we would never forget. Liliana, Giny and I stood watching them.

"What do you suppose made Kimo go after that other mongoose?" Liliana questioned.

"It is one of those things in nature which makes us guess, and whatever our conclusion may be, it is still a guess," I replied. "It may be that in his experience with Ewa Kimo has developed an affection for chickens in general."

"That would be contrary to instinct, though," Giny suggested.

"Yes, but animals often rise above instinct. They have the capacity to learn," I reasoned. "Of course, Kimo's fight may have been entirely from another motive. Perhaps it was a mating rival he eliminated."

"I don't like that angle so well," said Liliana. "It still leaves me wondering if Kimo is a threat to our neighbor's chickens. Oh—here's Hank!" There was a special warmth in her voice as she said this, and a smile that led Giny and me to look a question at each other.

Hank drove up as had been prearranged, and we were about to begin another day of activity on Maui. As he walked toward us, giving and receiving cheery greetings, a voice spoke out: "Wise guy! Aw, smart guy, eh?"

Hank seemed to flush, which is a rather difficult thing to do with his bronze complexion. He looked around quickly, the rest of us holding in our giggles.

"Yeh, smart guy, wise guy, wise guy," the calls went on. I felt sorry for Hank, knowing just how he felt. Surprise did not keep him in the dark for long. He flew out of a tree, lighting on Liliana's head, from which position he continued to talk in saucy tones. "Smart guy, eh? Wise guy."

"A fine greeting for a friend, isn't it, Hank?" Liliana said apologetically. "Did you think one of us was talking that way to you?"

"I wouldn't accuse you of that," Hank said, "but your friend did have me puzzled." Hank extended his hand to the bird, and merely stirred up more insulting remarks.

Moke came rushing up, bringing a letter which the mailman had just given him. "Read it, Mother, read it!" he cried excitedly. The letter was air mail, and to him that meant it came from Sam and Giny.

"But Sam and Giny are right here, Moke," she said. "They couldn't write to you."

"Oh," he said, as if surprised at the fact.

"Besides, this letter is for them, and we don't read other people's letters, do we?"

The letter was from Ada and Ray. We read it aloud, since it told of conditions and happenings in the north country that were a startling contrast to our surroundings. "Snow continues to fall every day," the letter ran. "We can't imagine where it all comes from, and certainly we don't know what to do with it. Not in years have we had such a snowy winter. We have shoveled out our walks about the house until we can no longer reach the top of the drifts. What do we do now? Snowplows have piled drifts so high at the side of the road that we cannot see cars as they go by. It is all very beautiful, but we think it could have been just as beautiful if there were a little less of it."

"And here we sit among orchids with summer all about us," Hank remarked. "It's hard to think of the country that letter described."

Liliana shivered a little. "Guess I am better suited to this," she said.

Moke tugged at her sleeve, requesting one of those whispered conferences. After an exchange in which she interpreted certain parts of the letter he didn't understand, she said, "Moke is concerned about Fiddlesticks and Freckles. How are they getting along in all that snow?"

"It speaks about them here," said Giny, turning a page.

"Forest animals are having a hard time," the letter

went on. "Loony Coon and his tribe are lucky they know how to hibernate. They can sleep until this is over—but Fiddlesticks and Freckles and the thousands of other deer are having trouble. We cannot get to the yarding place any more. The available food there was low. Now we are trying to get a plane to fly up from a hundred miles south and drop emergency food. All airfields up here are snowed under. The problem of placing such food properly is baffling. One little valley in that big woods is hard to find and identify from the air. All we say is that we will do everything we can to reach them."

The group was silent for a moment after Giny finished reading the letter. Hank spoke first. "That's tough country," he said with a shake of his head. "When will you know how those animals come through?"

"Not until the spring thaws open the country once more," I replied.

"Wise guy! Smart guy, eh?" came from overhead.

"Surprise, if you knew how lucky you are to live here, you'd be more polite," Liliana said, looking up at the black bird.

That day we drove to Hana, on the southeastern coast of Maui, over one of the most spectacular roads we have seen *anywhere*. It winds its way along the rugged sides of Haleakala, through verdant valleys, past waterfalls, into a luxurious land. Hana means "heavenly."

The next day our chosen route led us to the north

coast, and a second visit to Iao Valley to catch certain angles of it in different lighting. The day following was devoted to the region near Liliana's home at Lahaina. There we visited Lahainalune High School, the oldest school west of the Rockies, established in 1831. There too is found the largest banyan tree in all the islands, the site of an old fort built when Russia had some idea of taking over the islands, and a coastline of unsurpassed beauty. Liliana planned our days in such a way that very little of Maui's beauty escaped us. We understood why these island people had selected as their slogan *Maui no ka oi*—"Maui the best of all!"

The subject of our departure was never mentioned, though we all knew that the day was close at hand when we must leave. Back on the mainland Giny and I must take up a lecture tour. Hank's vacation was about over, and he must return to his work as a singer. Such a feeling of companionship had developed in our little circle that we all felt sad at the prospect of parting.

Our last evening together was spent on the beach. Hawaii turned loose all its charms. A great yellow moon hung in the eastern sky, laying a path of gold through the modest swells of the ocean. The mellow evening breeze gently rustled the wide leaves of coconut and date palms.

Conversation ceased; we were too engrossed in the beauty of the scene. Hank did the right thing, as Hank always does. He walked over to his car and returned with his ukulele. Seated on a lava rock, he sang several lovely songs. They were new to us and the words were Hawaiian.

Then, as if reading the request that was in my thoughts, he began singing the "Wedding Song." Liliana arose from her seat in the sands and walked toward him. Her voice took up the duet. There followed one of those rare experiences which surpass all human dreams or planning. The tropical loveliness of our surroundings, the spirit of friendliness that reigned, the beautiful blending of the two voices—all served to raise our thoughts high in the realm of joy and appreciation. To crown it all, little Moke stood up and, with a grace that could only come of his background, did his hula dance.

I looked at Liliana and Hank. What fine, young people they are, I thought. How happy they were together during these days! How much they had in common! Wouldn't it be wonderful, thought I, if they . . .

I glanced at Giny and we each knew what the other had been thinking.

"Sam Campbell, you mind your own business—strictly!" she said.

XXV

COMES ANOTHER SPRING

THE NORTH country slowly emerged from the snow-drifts and looked much bedraggled from the experience. Ice held long in the lakes, not entirely disappearing until the warm sun of April bathed the forests with its rays. Matted, brown, half-decayed leaves covered the forest floor. Lake levels were high and swamps were filled to overflowing with waters accumulated from melting snow. Wild geese were late in their northward flight, animals held on to hibernation, and spring was very late getting under way. The world had a hard time recovering from the winter of the big snow.

As soon as the lakes were open, Giny and I returned to our island home, bearing our memories of Hawaii. Song sparrows were there, their cheery songs compensating for the drab appearance of the woods. Loony Coon and several of his cohorts put in an appearance. They were as shaggy and untidy as the forest itself. Patty Sausage came out of her underground home, looking like a portion of a flat tire.

But nature will not tolerate being unbeautiful for long. Within several days we noticed a change in the trees. Buds were thickening on birches and aspens. Tiny green shoots knifed their way through matted leaves on the forest floor. Down in shallow waters we could see leaves of water lilies beginning to unfold. Little spring beauties bloomed as if by magic on sunny hillsides, and the trailing arbutus began lending its sweet fragrance to the forest breezes.

"Springtime is always lovely," said Giny one morning as we walked down a forest trail. "I would miss seasons greatly if we lived in Hawaii, wonderful as that place is."

"Really they have no seasons, have they? That is, not as we know seasons," I replied.

"No—a changing rainfall is about all the variation. They have rather a perpetual summer. The colors of autumn, the coziness and challenge of winter and the wonderful coming of spring—all this is lacking there."

"It's a grand place to visit," I commented.

"It *is*—and this is a grand place to *live*," Giny said, and then she added with emphasis, "for *us*."

"Good! If everyone wanted to live in the same spot, that place would certainly be overcrowded. Live here, and visit there whenever possible—that's a wonderful arrangement."

News was good from Hawaii. Scribbles from Moke, once deciphered, told us that Ewa and Kimo were getting along well. Kimo went away regularly for periods of two or three days, but returned. He stood high in favor with the neighbor now, for he had successfully battled a second mongoose caught approaching a chicken coop. Kimo was most welcome in the neighbor's house, and the shotgun was put away—at least, temporarily.

"And here is something Moke forgot to scribble," said Liliana in her letter. "I believe it will please you. Hank and I are going to do another duet. It will be a long duet—lifelong. We are so happy, and we are grateful to you for bringing us together."

A letter from Hank revealed his happiness. "Liliana and Moke are old and new Hawaii to me. I have never forgotten what you said that day on Haleakala, Sam. I am sure it helped prepare me for the happiness that is now unfolding."

"Yes, and I *did* mind my own business about them," I said to Giny after we had read this news.

"I wonder!" she said.

We saw very few deer in those first days in the woods. Occasionally we came on a yearling, but no large bucks and does. There were very discouraging reports of starvation among the animals. No doubt the deep snow had taken its toll.

We visited the places our two fawns had frequented the previous autumn. There were no tracks, of panther or deer either. We went to the Clearing, but it was lonely and empty.

One evening while twilight still held we walked to Vanishing Lake. Trilliums were appearing on the forest floor, and marsh marigolds blossomed in the lowlands. Spring peepers filled the air with their cries. The first whippoorwill was calling. We sat on a log looking toward the ridge where Bobette and her fawns were seen so often the previous year. The western sky was one vast orange glow, and the trees on top of the ridge stood out boldly against it.

Then out of the thicket at one side walked a deer the size of a yearling. Giny and I saw it at the same time. It made a beautiful picture against the orange sky. Feeding occasionally, it worked its way two thirds of the distance across the ridge.

"Could it be Freckles?" I whispered.

"Look—here comes another," said Giny in much excitement. "That walk! Sam, look! Is it he?"

The second creature walked out to where he showed up to advantage against the colorful sky. There he posed like a statue, head erect, even rigid, while he seemed to wait for the world to break out in applause. Then he moved on, every step looking as if it were practiced and posed. His front legs curled as he used them. With never a break in his pace, he strutted the entire length of the ridge.

"Oh, Fiddlesticks!" Giny burst forth. "It *is* Fiddlesticks, and Freckles, too. Sam, they've come through. They made it!"

Yes, they came through! My heart gave a few extra beats for pure joy. Our fawns had passed the perils of that hazardous first-year snow. True, the time before them had its problems and threats too. But they had grown in strength, wisdom, and experience, and their chances were good. Inanely I waved with both hands, half expecting them to rare up and wave back. They disappeared in the forest without even looking our way.

"Let's hurry home," I exclaimed, turning about.

"Why?"

"I want to get things ready to repair the screen door."

"And I must plant some flowers—Fiddlesticks may be hungry," Giny said, leading the way.

THE END
which is always
just a beginning